CATALYST
the prentice hall custom laboratory program for chemistry

Dr. Ted Marcus
Chemistry 110

Coastline Community College
Chemistry

Pearson Learning Solutions

New York   Boston   San Francisco
London   Toronto   Sydney   Tokyo   Singapore   Madrid
Mexico City   Munich   Paris   Cape Town   Hong Kong   Montreal

Senior Vice President, Editorial and Marketing: Patrick F. Boles
Executive Marketing Manager: Nathan L. Wilbur
Senior Acquisition Editor: Debbie Coniglio
Operations Manager: Eric M. Kenney
Development Editor: Christina Martin
Editorial Assistant: Jeanne Martin
Production Manager: Jennifer Berry
Art Director: Renée Sartell
Cover Designer: Kristen Kiley

Cover Art: Courtesy of Photodisc, Age Fotostock America, Inc. and Photo Researchers.

Pyrex, pHydrion, Chem3D Plus, Apple, Macintosh, Chemdraw, Hypercard, graphTool, Corning, Teflon, Mel-Temp, Rotaflow, Tygon, Spec20, and LambdaII UV/Vis are registered trademarks.

Chem3D Plus is a registered trademark of the Cambridge Soft Corp.

The information, illustration, and/or software contained in this book, and regarding the above mentioned programs, are provided "as is," without warranty of any kind, express or implied, including without limitation any warranty concerning the accuracy, adequacy, or completeness of such information. Neither the publisher, the authors, nor the copyright holders shall be responsible for any claims attributable to errors, omissions, or other inaccuracies contained in this book. Nor shall they be liable for direct, indirect, special, incidental, or consequential damages arising out of the use of such information or material.

The authors and publisher believe that the lab experiments described in this publication, when conducted in conformity with the safety precautions described herein and according to the school's laboratory safety procedures, are reasonably safe for the students for whom this manual is directed. Nonetheless, many of the described experiments are accompanied by some degree of risk, including human error, the failure or misuse of laboratory or electrical equipment, mismeasurement, spills of chemicals, and exposure to sharp objects, heat, body fluids, blood or other biologics. The authors and publisher disclaim any liability arising from such risks in connections with any of the experiments contained in this manual. If students have questions or problems with materials, procedures, or instructions on any experiment, they should always ask their instructor for help before proceeding.

This special edition published in cooperation with Pearson Learning Solutions.

Printed in the United States of America.
V092
Please visit our web site at *www.pearsoncustom.com/custom-library/catalyst*.

Attention bookstores: For permission to return any unsold stock, contact us at *pe-uscustomreturns@pearson.com*.

Pearson Learning Solutions, 501 Boylston Street, Suite 900, Boston, MA 02116
A Pearson Education Company
www.pearsoned.com

ISBN 10: 0-536-14514-8
ISBN 13: 978-0-536-14514-7

Laboratory Safety: General Guidelines

1. Notify your instructor immediately if you are pregnant, color blind, allergic to any insects or chemicals, taking immunosuppressive drugs, or have any other medical condition (such as diabetes, immunologic defect) that may require special precautionary measures in the laboratory.

2. Upon entering the laboratory, place all books, coats, purses, backpacks, etc. in designated areas, not on the bench tops.

3. Locate and, when appropriate, learn to use exits, fire extinguisher, fire blanket, chemical shower, eyewash, first aid kit, broken glass container, and cleanup materials for spills.

4. In case of fire, evacuate the room and assemble outside the building.

5. Do not eat, drink, smoke, or apply cosmetics in the laboratory.

6. Confine long hair, loose clothing, and dangling jewelry.

7. Wear shoes at all times in the laboratory.

8. Cover any cuts or scrapes with a sterile, waterproof bandage before attending lab.

9. Wear eye protection when working with chemicals.

10. Never pipet by mouth. Use mechanical pipeting devices.

11. Wash skin immediately and thoroughly if contaminated by chemicals or microorganisms.

12. Do not perform unauthorized experiments.

13. Do not use equipment without instruction.

14. Report *all* spills and accidents to your instructor immediately.

15. Never leave heat sources unattended.

16. When using hot plates, note that there is no visible sign that they are hot (such as a red glow). Always assume that hot plates are hot.

17. Use an appropriate apparatus when handling hot glassware.

18. Keep chemicals away from direct heat or sunlight.

19. Keep containers of alcohol, acetone, and other flammable liquids away from flames.

20. Do not allow any liquid to come into contact with electrical cords. Handle electrical connectors with dry hands. Do not attempt to disconnect electrical equipment that crackles, snaps, or smokes.

21. Upon completion of laboratory exercises, place all materials in the disposal areas designated by your instructor.

22. Do not pick up broken glassware with your hands. Use a broom and dustpan and discard the glass in designated glass waste containers; never discard with paper waste.

23. Wear disposable gloves when working with blood, other body fluids, or mucous membranes. Change gloves after possible contamination and wash hands immediately after gloves are removed.

24. The disposal symbol indicates that items that may have come in contact with body fluids should be placed in your lab's designated container. It also refers to liquid wastes that should not be poured down the drain into the sewage system.

25. Leave the laboratory clean and organized for the next student.

26. Wash your hands with liquid or powdered soap prior to leaving the laboratory.

27. The biohazard symbol indicates procedures that may pose health concerns.

The caution symbol points out instruments, substances, and procedures that require special attention to safety. These symbols appear throughout this manual.

Measurement Conversions

Metric to American Standard	American Standard to Metric
Length	
1 mm = 0.039 inches	1 inch = 2.54 cm
1 cm = 0.394 inches	1 foot = 0.305 m
1 m = 3.28 feet	1 yard = 0.914 m
1 m = 1.09 yards	1 mile = 1.61 km
Volume	
1 mL = 0.0338 fluid ounces	1 fluid ounce = 29.6 mL
1 L = 4.23 cups	1 cup = 237 mL
1 L = 2.11 pints	1 pint = 0.474 L
1 L = 1.06 quarts	1 quart = 0.947 L
1 L = 0.264 gallons	1 gallon = 3.79 L
Mass	
1 mg = 0.0000353 ounces	1 ounce = 28.3 g
1 g = 0.0353 ounces	1 pound = 0.454 kg
1 kg = 2.21 pounds	

Temperature

To convert temperature:

$$°C = \frac{5}{9}(F - 32) \qquad °F = \frac{9}{5}C + 32$$

°F °C

230 — 110
220
210 — 100 ← Water boils
200
190 — 90
 — 80
180
170 — 70
160
150
140 — 60
130
120 — 50
110
 — 40
98.6°F → 100 ← 37.0°C
Normal human body temperature   90 — 30   Normal human body temperature
80
70 — 20
60
50 — 10
40
30 — 0 ← Water freezes
20
10 — −10
0
 — −20
−10
−20 — −30
−30
−40 — −40

Centimeters   Inches

20 — 8
19
18 — 7
17
16
15 — 6
14
13 — 5
12
11
10 — 4
9
8 — 3
7
6
5 — 2
4
3 — 1
2
1
0 — 0

Contents

Goals

- Identify metric units used in measurement such as gram, meter, centimeter, millimeter, and milliliter.
- Correctly read a meterstick, a balance, and a graduated cylinder.
- State the correct number of significant figures in a measurement.

Discussion

Scientists and allied health personnel carry out laboratory procedures, take measurements, and report results accurately and clearly. How well they do these things can mean life or death to a patient. The system of measurement used in science, hospitals, and clinics is the metric system. The metric system is a *decimal system* in which measurements of each type are related by factors of 10. You use a decimal system when you change U.S. money. For example, 1 dime is the same as 10 cents or one cent is 1/10 of a dime. A dime and a cent are related by a factor of 10.

The metric system has one standard unit for each type of measurement. For example, the metric unit of length is the meter, whereas the U.S. system of measurement uses many units of length such as inch, foot, yard, and mile. Most of the rest of the world uses the metric system only. The most common metric units are listed in Table 1.

Table 1 *Metric Units*

Measurement	Metric Unit	Symbol
Length	meter	m
Mass	gram	g
Volume	liter	L
Temperature	degrees Celsius; kelvins	°C; K
Time	second	s

A unit must always be included when reporting a measurement. For example, 5.0 m indicates a quantity of 5.0 meters. Without the unit, we would not know the system of measurement used to obtain the number 5.0. It could have been 5.0 feet, 5.0 kilometers, or 5.0 inches. Thus, a unit is required to complete the measurement reported.

For larger and smaller measurements, prefixes are attached in front of the standard unit. Some prefixes such as *kilo* are used for larger quantities; other prefixes such as *milli* are used for smaller quantities. The most common prefixes are listed in Table 2.

Table 2 *Some Prefixes in the Metric System*

Prefix	Symbol	Meaning
kilo	k	1000
deci	d	0.1 (1/10)
centi	c	0.01 (1/100)
milli	m	0.001 (1/1000)

Measured and Exact Numbers

When we measure the length, volume, or mass of an object, the numbers we report are called *measured numbers*. Suppose you got on a scale this morning and saw that you weighed 145 lb. The scale is a measuring tool and your weight is a measured number. Each time we use a measuring tool to determine a quantity, the result is a measured number.

Exact numbers are obtained when we count objects. Suppose you counted 5 beakers in your laboratory drawer. The number 5 is an exact number. You did not use a measuring tool to obtain the number. Exact numbers are also found in the numbers that define a relationship between two metric units or between two U.S. units. For example, the numbers in the following definitions are exact: 1 meter is equal to 100 cm; 1 foot has 12 inches. See Sample Problem 1.

Sample Problem 1

Describe each of the following as a measured or exact number:

a. 14 inches   b. 14 pencils   c. 60 minutes in 1 hour   d. 7.5 kg

Solution:

a. measured   b. exact   c. exact (definition)   d. measured

Significant Figures in Measurements

In measured numbers, all the reported figures are called *significant figures*. The first significant figure is the first nonzero digit. The last significant figure is always the estimated digit. Zeros between other digits or at the end of a decimal number are counted as significant figures. However, leading zeros are *not significant;* they are placeholders. Zeros are *not significant* in large numbers with no decimal points; they are placeholders needed to express the magnitude of the number.

When a number is written in scientific notation, all the figures in the coefficient are significant. Examples of counting significant figures in measured numbers are in Table 3 and Sample Problem 2.

Table 3   *Examples of Counting Significant Figures*

Measurement	Number of Significant Figures	Reason
455.2 cm	4	All nonzero digits are significant.
0.80 m	2	A following zero in a decimal number is significant.
50.2 L	3	A zero between nonzero digits is significant.
0.0005 lb	1	Leading zeros are not significant.
25,000 ft	2	Placeholder zeros are not significant.

Sample Problem 2

State the number of significant figures in each of the following measured numbers:

a. 0.00580 m   b. 132.08 g

Solution:

a. Three significant figures. The zeros after the decimal point are placeholder zeros, but the zero following nonzero digits is *significant.*
b. Five significant figures. The zero between nonzero digits is significant.

When you use a meterstick or read the volume in a graduated cylinder, the measurement must be reported as precisely as possible. The number of *significant figures* you can report depends on the lines marked on the measuring tool you use. For example, on a 50-mL graduated cylinder, the small lines represent a 1-mL volume. If the liquid level is between 21 mL and 22 mL, you know you can report 21 mL for certain. However, you can add one more digit (*the last digit*) to your reported value by estimating between the 1-mL lines. For example, if the volume level were halfway between the 21-mL and 22-mL lines, you would report the volume as 21.5 mL. If the volume level *is exactly* on the 21-mL line, you indicate this precision by adding a *significant zero* to give a measured volume of 21.0 mL.

A. Measuring Length

The standard unit of length in the metric system is the *meter* (*m*). Using an appropriate prefix, you can indicate a length that is greater or less than a meter as listed in Table 4. Kilometers are used in most countries for measuring the distance between two cities, whereas centimeters or millimeters are used for small lengths.

Table 4 *Some Metric Units Used to Measure Length*

Length	Symbol	Meaning
1 kilometer	km	1000 meters (m)
1 decimeter	dm	0.1 m (1/10 m)
1 centimeter	cm	0.01 m (1/100 m)
1 millimeter	mm	0.001 m (1/1000 m)

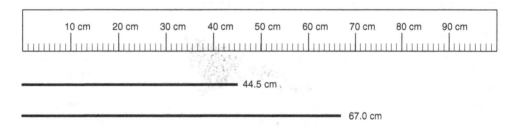

Figure 1 A meterstick divided into centimeters (cm)

A *meterstick* is divided into 100 cm as seen in Figure 1. The smallest lines are centimeters. That means that each measurement you make can be certain to the centimeter. The final digit in a precise measurement is obtained by estimating. For example, the shorter line in Figure 1 reaches the 44-cm mark and is about halfway to 45 cm. We report its length as 44.5 cm. The last digit (0.5) is the estimated digit. If the line appears to end at a centimeter mark, then the estimated digit is 0.0 cm. The longer line in Figure 1 appears to end right at the 67-cm line, which is indicated by reporting its length as 67.0 cm.

B. Measuring Volume

The volume of a substance measures the space it occupies. In the metric system, the unit for volume is the *liter* (*L*). Prefixes are used to express smaller volumes such as deciliters (dL) or milliliters (mL). One cubic centimeter (cm^3 or cc) is equal to 1 mL. The terms are used interchangeably. See Table 5.

Table 5 *Some Metric Units Used to Measure Volume*

Unit of Volume	Symbol	Meaning
1 kiloliter	kL	1000 liters (L)
1 deciliter	dL	0.1 L (1/10 L)
1 milliliter	mL	0.001 L (1/1000 L)

In the laboratory, the volume of a liquid is measured in a graduated cylinder (Figure 2). Set the cylinder on a level surface and bring your eyes even with the liquid level. Notice that the water level is not a straight line but curves downward in the center. This curve, called a *meniscus,* is read at its lowest point (center) to obtain the correct volume measurement for the liquid. In this graduated cylinder, the volume of the liquid is 42.0 mL.

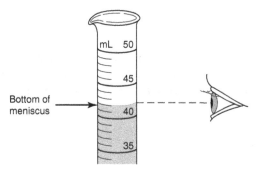

Figure 2 Reading a volume of 42.0 mL in a graduated cylinder

On large cylinders, the lines may represent volumes of 2 mL, 5 mL, or 10 mL. On a 250-mL cylinder, the marked lines usually represent 5 mL. On a 1000-mL cylinder, each line may be 10 mL. Then your precision on a measurement will be to the milliliter or mL.

C. Measuring Mass

The *mass* of an object indicates the amount of matter present in that object. The *weight* of an object is a measure of the attraction that Earth has for that object. Because this attraction is proportional to the mass of the object, we will use the terms *mass* and *weight* interchangeably.

In the metric system, the unit of mass is the *gram (g)*. A larger unit, the *kilogram (kg)*, is used in measuring a patient's weight in a hospital. A smaller unit of mass, the *milligram (mg)*, is often used in the laboratory. See Table 6.

Table 6 *Some Metric Units Used to Measure Mass*

Mass	Symbol	Meaning
kilogram	kg	1000 g
gram	g	1000 mg
milligram	mg	1/1000 g (0.001 g)

Lab Information

Time: 2 hr

Comments: Tear out the report sheets and place them beside the experimental procedures
as you work.
Determine the markings on each measuring tool before you measure.
Record all the possible numbers for a measurement including an estimated digit.
Write a unit of measurement after each measured number.

Related Topics: Significant figures, measured and exact numbers, metric prefixes

Experimental Procedures

A. Measuring Length

Materials: Meterstick, string

A.1 Observe the marked lines on a meterstick. Identify the lines that represent centimeters and millimeters. Determine how you will estimate between the smallest lines.

A.2 Use the meterstick to make the length measurements (cm) indicated on the report sheet. String may be used to determine the distance around your wrist. Include the estimated digit in each measurement.

A.3 Indicate the estimated digit and the number of significant figures in each measurement. See Sample Problem 3.

Sample Problem 3
What is the estimated digit in each of the following measured masses?
a. beaker 42.18 g   b. pencil 11.6 g

Solution:
a. hundredths place (0.08 g)   b. tenths place (0.6 g)

A.4 Measure the length of the line on the report sheet. List the measurements of the same line obtained by other students in the lab.

B. Measuring Volume

Materials: Display of graduated cylinders with liquids, 50-mL, 100-mL, 250-mL, and 500-mL (or larger) graduated cylinders, test tube, solid object

B.1 **Volume of a liquid** Determine the volumes of the liquids in a display of graduated cylinders. Be as precise as you can. For example, each line marked on a 50-mL graduated cylinder measures 1 mL. By estimating the volume *between* the 1-mL markings, you can report a volume to a tenth (0.1) of a milliliter. Indicate the estimated digit and the number of significant figures in each measurement.

B.2 **Volume of a test tube** Fill a small test tube to the rim. Carefully pour the water into a small graduated cylinder. State the volume represented by the smallest marked lines on the cylinder. Record the volume of the water and state the estimated digit. Fill the test tube again and pour the water into a medium-sized graduated cylinder. Record. Repeat this process using a large graduated cylinder. Record.

B.3 **Volume of a solid by volume displacement** When an object is submerged in water, it displaces its own volume of water, causing the water level to rise. The volume of the object is the difference in the water level before and after the object is submerged. See Figure 3.

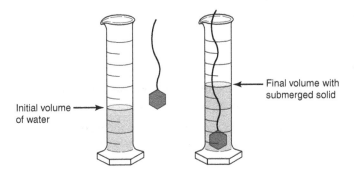

Figure 3 Using volume displacement to determine the volume of a solid

Obtain a graduated cylinder that will hold the solid. Place water in the graduated cylinder until it is about half full. Carefully record the volume of water. Tie a piece of thread around a heavy solid object. Slowly submerge the solid under the water. Record the new volume of the water. Calculate the volume (mL) displaced by the solid.

C. Measuring Mass

Materials: Balance, objects to weigh (beaker, rubber stopper, evaporating dish), unknown mass

C.1 After your instructor shows you how to use a laboratory balance, determine the mass of the listed objects from your lab drawer. If you are using a triple beam balance, be sure that all of your recorded measurements include an estimated digit.

C.2 Now that you have used the balance several times, obtain an object of unknown mass from your instructor. Record the code number and determine its mass. Record. Check your result with the instructor.

Goals

- Calculate the density of a substance from measurements of its mass and volume.
- Calculate the specific gravity of a liquid from its density.
- Determine the specific gravity of a liquid using a hydrometer.

Discussion

A.   Density of a Solid

To determine the density of a substance, you need to measure both its mass and its volume. You have carried out both of these procedures in previous labs. From the mass and volume, the density is calculated. If the mass is measured in grams and the volume in milliliters, the density will have the units of g/mL.

$$\text{Density of a substance} \; = \; \frac{\text{Mass of substance}}{\text{Volume of substance}} \; = \; \frac{\text{g of substance}}{\text{mL of substance}}$$

B.   Density of a Liquid

To determine the density of a liquid, you need the mass and volume of the liquid. The mass of a liquid is determined by weighing. The mass of a container is obtained and then a certain volume of liquid is added and the combined mass determined. Subtracting the mass of the container gives the mass of the liquid. From the mass and volume, the density is calculated.

$$\text{Density of liquid} \; = \; \frac{\text{Mass (g) of liquid}}{\text{Volume (mL) of liquid}}$$

C.   Specific Gravity

The specific gravity of a liquid is a comparison of the density of that liquid with the density of water, which is 1.00 g/mL (4°C).

$$\text{Specific gravity (sp gr)} \; = \; \frac{\text{Density of liquid (g/mL)}}{\text{Density of water (1.00 g/mL)}}$$

Specific gravity is a number with no units; the units of density (g/mL) have canceled out. This is one of the few measurements in chemistry written without any units.

Using a hydrometer The specific gravity of a fluid is determined by using a hydrometer. Small hydrometers (urinometers) are used in the hospital to determine the specific gravity of urine. Another type of hydrometer is used to measure the specific gravity of the fluid in your car battery. A hydrometer placed in a liquid is spun slowly to keep it from sticking to the sides of the container. The scale on the hydrometer is read at the lowest (center) point of the meniscus of the fluid. Read the specific gravity on the hydrometer to 0.001. See Figure 1.

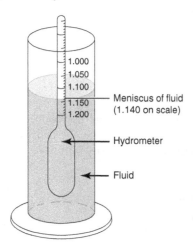

Figure 1 Measuring specific gravity using a hydrometer

D.   Graphing Mass and Volume

When a group of experimental quantities are determined, a graph can be prepared that gives a pictorial representation of the data. After a data table is prepared, a series of steps are followed to construct a graph.

Lab Information

Time: 3 hr

Comments: Tear out the report sheets and place them beside the procedures.
               Round off the calculator answers to the correct number of significant figures.
               Dispose of liquids properly as directed by your instructor.

Related Topics: Mass, volume, prefixes, significant figures, density, specific gravity

Experimental Procedures      GOGGLES REQUIRED!

A.   Density of a Solid

   Materials: Metal object, string or thread, graduated cylinder

A.1 **Mass of the solid** Obtain a solid metal object. Determine its mass and record.

A.2 **Volume of the solid by displacement** Obtain a graduated cylinder that is large enough to hold the solid metal object. Add water until the cylinder is about half full. Read the water level carefully and record. If the solid object is heavy, lower it into the water by attaching a string or thread. While the solid object is submerged in the water, record the final water level. Calculate the volume of the solid.

Volume of solid = Final water level – initial water level

A.3 **Calculating the density of the solid** Calculate the density (g/mL) of the solid by dividing its mass (g) by its volume (mL). Be sure to determine the correct number of significant figures in your calculated density value.

$$\text{Density of solid} = \frac{\text{Mass (g) of solid}}{\text{Volume (mL) of solid}}$$

A.4 If your instructor indicates that the solid is made of one of the substances in Table 1, use the density you calculated in A.3 to identify the metal from the known values for density.

Table 1 *Density Values of Some Metals*

Substance	Density (g/mL)
Aluminum	2.7
Brass	8.4
Copper	8.9
Iron	7.9
Lead	11.3
Nickel	8.9
Tin	7.3
Zinc	7.1

B. Density of a Liquid

Materials: 50-mL graduated cylinder, two liquid samples, 100-mL or 250-mL beaker

B.1 **Volume of liquid** Place about 20 mL of water in a 50-mL graduated cylinder. Record. *(Do not use the markings on beakers to measure volume; they are not precise.)*

B.2 **Mass of liquid** The mass of a liquid is found by weighing by difference. First, determine the mass of a small, dry beaker. Pour the liquid into the beaker, and reweigh. Record the combined mass. *Be sure to write down all the figures in the measurements.* Calculate the mass of the liquid.

> *Taring a container on an electronic balance:* The mass of a container on an electronic balance can be set to 0 by pressing the *tare* bar. As a substance is added to the container, the mass shown on the readout is for the *substance* only. (When a container is *tared,* it is not necessary to subtract the mass of the beaker.)

B.3 **Density of liquid** Calculate the density of the liquid by dividing its mass (g) by the volume (mL) of the liquid.

$$\text{Density of liquid} = \frac{\text{Mass (g) of liquid}}{\text{Volume (mL) of liquid}}$$

Repeat the same procedure for another liquid provided in the laboratory.

C. Specific Gravity

Materials: Water, liquids used in part B in graduated cylinders with hydrometers

C.1 Calculate the specific gravity (sp gr) of each liquid you used in B. Divide its density by the standard density of water (1.00 g/mL).

$$\text{Specific gravity} = \frac{\text{Density of a substance (g/mL)}}{\text{Density of water (1.00 g/mL)}}$$

C.2 Read the hydrometer set in a graduated cylinder containing the same liquid you used in the density section. Record. Some hydrometers use the European decimal point, which is a comma. The value 1,000 on a European scale is read as 1.000. Record specific gravity as a decimal number.

D. Graphing Mass and Volume

Materials: Metal pieces such as aluminum, copper, or zinc or pennies (pre-1980 or post-1980) 50-mL graduated cylinder

In this graphing activity, we will show the relationship between the mass and volume of a substance. The volume and mass of five different samples of the same substance will be measured. After the data for the samples are collected, the mass and volume of each sample will be used to prepare a graph. The density (g/mL) will be visually represented on a graph.

D.1 Place about 20–25 mL of water in a 50-mL graduated cylinder. Carefully record the initial volume of water.

D.2 Place the cylinder and water on a top-loading balance and determine their mass. Record. Use the same balance to complete the experiment.

D.3 Add two or three pieces of metal or pennies. Record the new level of the water. Record the new mass. Subtract the initial volume of water from this water level to determine the volume of the metal pieces or the pennies. If you did not tare the cylinder and water originally, determine the mass of the metal pieces or pennies by subtracting the initial mass from this combined mass. Add some more pieces of metal or some more pennies to the cylinder. Each time record the resulting water level and the new mass. Repeat this process for a total of five sets of data.

D.4 Prepare a graph by plotting the mass (g) of the metal pieces or pennies on the vertical axis and the volume (mL) of the metal pieces or pennies on the horizontal axis. Use a ruler to draw a line through the points you have plotted. If some of the points fall off the line, run the line between them so you have as many points above the line as you have below the line. Draw a smooth line through the points.

D.5 The slope of the line on the graph represents the density of the metal. Mark two places on the line. Divide the difference between the two mass values by the difference of the two values for volume.

$$\frac{\text{Mass (2)} - \text{Mass (1)}}{\text{Volume (2)} - \text{Volume (1)}} = \frac{\text{g}}{\text{mL}} = \text{density of metal or pennies}$$

Atomic Structure

Goals

- Write the correct symbols or names of some elements.
- Describe some physical properties of the elements you observe.
- Categorize an element as a metal or nonmetal from its physical properties.
- Given the complete symbol of an atom, determine its mass number, atomic number, and the number of protons, neutrons, and electrons.

Discussion

Primary substances, called elements, build all the materials about you. Some look similar, but others look unlike anything else. In this experiment, you will describe the physical properties of elements in a laboratory display and determine the location of elements on a blank periodic table.

A. Physical Properties of Elements

Metals are elements that are usually shiny or have a metallic luster. They are usually good conductors of heat and electricity, ductile (can be drawn into a wire), and malleable (can be molded into a shape). Some metals such as sodium or calcium may have a white coating of oxide formed by reacting with oxygen in the air. If these are cut, you can see the fresh shiny metal underneath. In contrast, nonmetals are not good conductors of heat and electricity, are brittle (not ductile), and appear dull, not shiny.

B. Periodic Table

The periodic table, shown on the inside front cover of this lab manual and your textbook, contains information about each of the elements. On the table, the horizontal rows are *periods,* and the vertical columns are *groups.* Each group contains elements that have similar physical and chemical properties. The groups are numbered across the top of the chart. Elements in Group 1 are the *alkali metals,* elements in Group 2 are the *alkaline earths,* and Group 7 contains the *halogens.* Group 8 contains the *noble gases,* which are elements that are not very reactive compared to other elements. A dark zigzag line that looks like a staircase separates the *metals* on the left side from the *nonmetals* on the right side.

C. Subatomic Particles

There are different kinds of atoms for each of the elements. Atoms are made up of smaller bits of matter called *subatomic particles. Protons* are positively charged particles, *electrons* are negatively charged, and *neutrons* are neutral (no charge). In an atom, the protons and neutrons are tightly packed in the tiny center called the *nucleus.* Most of the atom is empty space, which contains fast-moving electrons. Electrons are so small that their mass is considered to be negligible compared to the mass of the proton or neutron. The *atomic number* is equal to the number of protons. The *mass number* of an atom is the number of protons and neutrons.

atomic number = number of protons (p^+)
mass number = sum of the number of protons and neutrons ($p^+ + n^0$)

From *Laboratory Manual for General, Organic, & Biological Chemistry,* Karen C. Timberlake. Copyright © 2002 Pearson Education, Inc., publishing as Benjamin Cummings. All rights reserved.

D. Isotopes

Isotopes are atoms of the same element that differ in the number of neutrons. This means that isotopes of an element have the same number of protons, but different mass numbers. The following example represents the symbol of a sulfur isotope that has 16 protons and 18 neutrons.

Complete Symbol of an Isotope **Meaning**

mass number (p^+ and n^0) → **34** This atom has 16 protons and 18 neutrons.

      symbol of element → **S** The element is sulfur.

atomic number (p^+) → **16** The atom has 16 protons.

Lab Information

Time: 2 hr

Comments: Obtain a periodic table as a reference.
Tear out the report sheets and place them beside the procedures.
Carefully observe the physical properties of the elements in the display.

Related Topics: Names and symbols of the elements, periodic table, atoms, subatomic particles, isotopes, electrons and protons

Experimental Procedures

A. Physical Properties of Elements

Materials: A display of elements

Observe the elements in the laboratory display of elements. In the report sheet, write the symbol and atomic number for each element listed. Describe some physical properties such as color and luster. From your observations, identify each element as a metal (M) or a nonmetal (NM).

B. Periodic Table

Materials: Periodic table, colored pencils, display of elements

B.1 On the incomplete periodic table provided in the report sheet, write the atomic numbers and symbols of the elements you observed in part A. Write the group number at the top of each column of the representative (Groups 1–8) elements. Write the period numbers for each of the horizontal rows shown. Using different colors, shade in the columns that contain the alkali metals, alkaline earths, halogens, and noble gases. With another color, shade in the transition elements. Draw a heavy line to separate the metals and nonmetals.

B.2 *Without looking* at the display of elements, use the periodic table to decide whether the elements listed on the report sheet would be metals or nonmetals; shiny or dull. *After* you complete your predictions, observe those same elements in the display to see if you predicted correctly.

C. Subatomic Particles

For each of the neutral atoms described in the table, write the atomic number, mass number, and number of protons, neutrons, and electrons.

D. Isotopes

Complete the information for each of the isotopes of calcium: the complete nuclear symbol and the number of protons, neutrons, and electrons.

Electron Configuration and Periodic Properties

Goals

- Describe the color of a flame produced by an element.
- Use the color of a flame to identify an element.
- Write the electron configuration for an element.
- Draw a graph of atomic diameter against atomic number.
- Interpret the trends in atomic radii within a family and a period.

Discussion

A. Flame Tests

The chemistry of an element strongly depends on the arrangement of the electrons. The energy levels for electrons of atoms of the *first 20 elements* have the following number of electrons.

Electron Arrangement for Elements 1–20
Level 1 $(2e^-)$ Level 2 $(8e^-)$ Level 3 $(8e^-)$ Level 4 $(2e^-)$

When electrons absorb specific amounts of energy, they can attain higher energy levels. In order to return to the lower, more stable energy levels, electrons release energy. If the energy released is the same amount as the energy that makes up visible light, the element produces a color.

When heated, many of the elements in Groups 1a and 2a produce colorful flames. Each element produces a characteristic color. When the light from one of these flames passes through a glass prism or crystal, a series of color lines appears. The spaces between lines appear dark. Such a series of lines, known as a *spectrum,* is used to identify elements in water, food, the sun, stars, and on other planets.

B. Electron Configuration

In an electron configuration, electrons are arranged by subshells starting with the lowest energy. The number of electrons in each subshell is written as a superscript. The electron arrangement of an element is related to its position in the periodic table. The electron configuration can be written by following the subshell blocks across the periodic table starting with period 1. The *s* **block** is formed by Groups 1A and 2A. The *p* **block** includes the elements in Groups 3A to 8A. The period number gives the particular energy level of each p subshell beginning with $2p$. Examples are as follows:

Li $1s^22s^1$	**O** $1s^22s^22p^4$	**Ne** $1s^22s^22p^6$
Na $1s^22s^22p^63s^1$	**S** $1s^22s^22p^63s^23p^4$	**Ar** $1s^22s^22p^63s^23p^6$

On the periodic table, the 4s block fills next

K $1s^22s^22p^63s^23p^64s^1$	**Ca** $1s^22s^22p^63s^23p^64s^2$

The d block begins with atomic number 21 and includes ten transition metals. The energy level of each d block is one less than its period number.

Sc $1s^22s^22p^63s^23p^64s^23d^1$	**Fe** $1s^22s^22p^63s^23p^64s^23d^6$	**Zn** $1s^22s^22p^63s^23p^64s^23d^{10}$
Ga $1s^22s^22p^63s^23p^64s^23d^{10}4p^1$		**As** $1s^22s^22p^63s^23p^64s^23d^{10}4p^3$
Br $1s^22s^22p^63s^23p^64s3d^{10}4p^5$		**Kr** $1s^22s^22p^63s^23p^64s^23d^{10}4p^6$

The *f* **block**, which has a maximum of 14 electrons, follows the 6s block. The energy level of each *f* block is two less than the corresponding period number.

C.   Graphing a Periodic Property: Atomic Radius

Since the 1800s scientists have recognized that chemical and physical properties of certain groups of elements tend to be similar. A Russian scientist, Dmitri Mendeleev, found that the chemical properties of elements tended to recur when the elements were arranged in order of increasing atomic mass. This repetition of similar characteristics is called periodic behavior. He used this periodic pattern to predict the characteristics of elements that were not yet discovered. Later, H. G. Moseley established that the similarities in properties were associated with the atomic number.

In the electron arrangement of an element, the electrons in the highest or outermost energy level are called the valence electrons. The valence electrons determine the chemical properties of the elements. If the elements are grouped according to the number of valence electrons, their chemical and physical properties are similar. The similarities of behavior occur periodically as the number of valence electrons is repeated.

In this exercise, you will graph the relationship between the atomic radius of an atom and its atomic number. Such a graph will show a repeating or periodic trend. Observe the graph in Figure 1, which was obtained by plotting the average temperature of the seasons. The graph shows that a cycle of high and low temperatures repeats each year. Such a tendency is known as a periodic property. There are three cycles on this particular graph, one full cycle occurring every year. When such cycles are known, the average temperatures for the next year could be predicted.

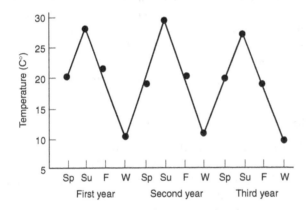

Figure 1 A graph of average seasonal temperatures.

Lab Information

Time: $1\frac{1}{2}$ hr

Comments: Obtain a periodic table or use the inside cover of your textbook.
                     Tear out the report sheets and place them beside the procedures.
                     In neutral atoms, the number of electrons is equal to the number of protons.

Related Topics: Electrons and protons, energy levels, and electron arrangement

Experimental Procedures

 **GOGGLES REQUIRED!**

A. Flame Tests

Materials: Bunsen burner, spot plate, flame-test (nichrome) wire, cork, 100-mL beaker, 1 M HCl, 0.1 M solutions (dropper bottles): $CaCl_2$, KCl, $BaCl_2$, $SrCl_2$, $CuCl_2$, NaCl, and unknown solutions

Obtain a spot plate, flame-test wire, and cork stopper. Bend one end of the flame-test wire into a small loop and secure the other end in a cork stopper. Pour a small amount of 1 M HCl into a 100-mL beaker. Rinse the spot plate in distilled water. Place 6–8 drops of each test solution in separate indentations of the spot plate. Label the spot plate diagram in the laboratory report to match the solutions. Be careful not to mix the different solutions.

CAUTION 1 M HCl is corrosive! Be careful when you use it. Wash off any HCl spills on the skin with tap water for 10 minutes.

Adjust the flame of a Bunsen burner until it is nearly colorless. Clean the test wire by dipping the loop in the HCl in the beaker and placing it in the flame of the Bunsen burner. If you see a strong color in the flame while heating the wire, dip it in the HCl again. Repeat until the color is gone.

Observing Flame Colors

Dip the cleaned wire in one of the solutions on the spot plate. Make sure that a thin film of the solution adheres to the loop. See Figure 2. Move the loop of the wire into the lower portion of the flame and record the color you observe. For each solution, it is the first element in the formula that is responsible for color.

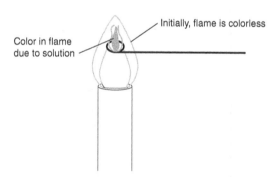

Color in flame due to solution

Initially, flame is colorless

Figure 2 Using a flame-test wire to test for flame color

Note: The color of potassium in the KCl flame is short-lived. Be sure to observe the color of the flame from the KCl solution within the first few seconds of heating. Repeat each flame test until you can describe the color of the flame produced. Clean the wire and repeat the flame test with the other solutions.

Identifying Solutions

Obtain unknown solutions as indicated by your instructor and record their code letters. Place 6–8 drops of each unknown solution in a clean spot plate. Use the flame-test procedure to determine the identity of the unknown solution. You may wish to recheck the flame color of the known solution that best matches the flame color of an unknown. For example, if you think your unknown is KCl, recheck the color of the KCl solution to confirm.

B. Electron Configuration

Write the electron configuration of each atom listed on the laboratory report. Indicate the number of valence electrons and the group number for the element.

C. Graphing a Periodic Property: Atomic Radius

The atomic radii for elements with atomic numbers 1–25 are listed in Table 1. On the graph, plot the atomic radius of each element against the atomic number of the element on the graph. Be sure to connect the points. Use the completed graph to answer questions in the report sheet about valence electrons and group number.

Table 1 Atomic Radii for the Elements with Atomic Numbers 1–25

Element	Symbol	Atomic Number	Atomic Radius (pm*)
first period			
hydrogen	H	1	37
helium	He	2	50
second period			
lithium	Li	3	152
beryllium	Be	4	111
boron	B	5	88
carbon	C	6	77
nitrogen	N	7	70
oxygen	O	8	66
fluorine	F	9	64
neon	Ne	10	70
third period			
sodium	Na	11	186
magnesium	Mg	12	160
aluminum	Al	13	143
silicon	Si	14	117
phosphorus	P	15	110
sulfur	S	16	104
chlorine	Cl	17	99
argon	Ar	18	94
fourth period			
potassium	K	19	231
calcium	Ca	20	197
scandium	Sc	21	160
titanium	Ti	22	150
vanadium	V	23	135
chromium	Cr	24	125
manganese	Mn	25	125

*(picometer = 10^{-12} m)

Goals

- Compare physical properties of a compound with the properties of the elements that formed it.
- Identify a compound as ionic or covalent.
- Determine the subscripts in the formula of a compound.
- Write the electron-dot structure for an atom and an ion.
- Write a correct formula and name of an ionic or covalent compound.
- Write a correct formula and name of a compound containing a polyatomic ion.

Discussion

Nearly everything is made of compounds. A compound consists of two or more different elements that are chemically combined. Most atoms form compounds by forming octets in their outer shells. The attractions between the atoms are called *chemical bonds*. For example, when a metal combines with a nonmetal, the metal loses electrons to form a positive ion and the nonmetal gains electrons to form a negative ion. The attraction between the positive ions and the negative ions is called an *ionic bond*. When two nonmetals form a compound, they share electrons and form *covalent bonds*. In covalent compounds, the atoms are bonded as individual units called *molecules*. See Table 1.

Table 1 *Types of Bonding in Compounds*

Compound	Types of Elements	Characteristics	Type of Bonding
$NaCl$	Metal, nonmetal	Ions (Na^+, Cl^-)	Ionic
$MgBr_2$	Metal, nonmetal	Ions (Mg^{2+}, Br^-)	Ionic
CCl_4	Two nonmetals	Molecules	Covalent
NH_3	Two nonmetals	Molecules	Covalent

In a compound, there is a definite proportion of each element. This is represented in the formula, which gives the lowest whole number ratio of each kind of atom. For example, water has the formula H_2O. This means that two atoms of hydrogen and one atom of oxygen are combined in every molecule of water. Water never has any other formula.

When we observe a compound or an element, we see physical properties such as color and luster. We measure other physical properties such as density, melting point, and boiling point. When elements undergo chemical combination, the physical properties change to the physical properties of the new substances that form. For example, when silver tarnishes, the physical property of the shiny, silver metal changes to the dull, gray color as silver combines with sulfur to form tarnish, Ag_2S. A chemical change has occurred when the reaction between elements causes a change in their physical properties.

A. Electron-Dot Structures

When atoms of metals in Groups 1, 2, or 3 react with atoms of nonmetals in Groups 5, 6, or 7, the metals lose electrons and the nonmetals gain electrons in their valence shells. We can predict the number of electrons lost or gained by analyzing the electron-dot structures of the atoms. In an electron-dot structure, the valence electrons are represented as dots around the symbol of the atom. For example, calcium, electron arrangement 2-8-8-2, has two valence electrons and an electron-dot structure with two dots. Chlorine, electron arrangement 2-8-7, has seven valence electrons and an electron-dot structure with seven dots.

Ca • $\overset{\bullet\bullet}{\underset{\bullet\bullet}{:}}$ Cl •

Ca loses two electrons to attain an octet. This gives it an ionic charge of 2+. It is now a calcium ion with an electron arrangement of 2-8-8. As a positive ion, it keeps the same name as the element.

	Calcium Atom, Ca	**Calcium Ion, Ca^{2+}**	
Electron arrangement	2-8-8-2	2-8-8	(Two electrons lost)
Number of protons	$20p^+$	$20p^+$	(Same)
Number of electrons	$20e^-$	$18e^-$	(Two fewer electrons)
Net ionic charge	0	2+	

When nonmetals (5, 6, or 7 valence electrons) combine with metals, they gain electrons to become stable, and form negatively charged ions. For example, a chlorine atom gains one valence electron to become stable with an electron arrangement of 2-8-8. With the addition of one electron, chlorine becomes a chloride ion with an ionic charge of 1–. In the name of a binary compound with two different elements, the name of the negative ion ends in *ide*.

	Chlorine Atom, Cl	**Chloride Ion, Cl$^-$**	
Electron arrangement	2-8-7	2-8-8	(Electron added)
Number of protons	$17p^+$	$17p^+$	(Same)
Number of electrons	$17e^-$	$18e^-$	(One more electron)
Net ionic charge	0	1–	

B. Ionic Compounds and Formulas

The group number on the periodic table can be used to determine the ionic charges of elements in each family of elements. *Nonmetals form ions when they combine with a metal.*

Group number	*1*	*2*	*3*	*4*	*5*	*6*	*7*	*8*
Valence electrons	$1e^-$	$2e^-$	$3e^-$	$4e^-$	$5e^-$	$6e^-$	$7e^-$	$8e^-$
Electron change	lose 1	lose 2	lose 3	none	gain 3	gain 2	gain 1	no change
Ionic charge	1+	2+	3+	none	3–	2–	1–	none

In an ionic formula, the *number of electrons lost is equal to the number of electrons gained*. The overall net charge is zero. To balance the charge, we must determine the smallest number of positive and negative ions that give an overall charge of zero (0). We can illustrate the process by representing the ions Ca^{2+} and Cl$^-$ as geometric shapes.

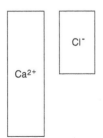

The charge is balanced by using two Cl^- ions to match the charge of the Ca^{2+} ion. The number of ions needed gives the subscripts in the formula for the compound $CaCl_2$. (The subscript 1 for Ca is understood.) In any ionic formula, *only the symbols are written, not their ionic charges.*

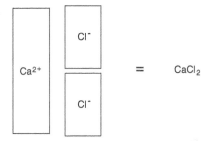

C. Ionic Compounds with Transition Metals

Most of the transition metals can form more than one kind of positive ion. We will illustrate variable valence with iron. Iron forms two ions, one (Fe^{2+}) with a 2+ charge, and another (Fe^{3+}) with a 3+ charge. To distinguish between the two ions, a Roman numeral that gives the ionic charge of that particular ion follows the element name. The Roman numeral is always included in the names of compounds with variable positive ions. In an older naming system, the ending *ous* indicates the lower valence; the ending *ic* indicates the higher one. See Table 2.

Table 2 *Some Ions of the Transition Elements*

Ion	Names	Compound	Names
Fe^{2+}	Iron(II) ion or ferrous ion	$FeCl_2$	Iron(II) chloride or ferrous chloride
Fe^{3+}	Iron(III) ion or ferric ion	$FeCl_3$	Iron(III) chloride or ferric chloride
Cu^+	Copper(I) ion or cuprous ion	$CuCl$	Copper(I) chloride or cuprous chloride
Cu^{2+}	Copper(II) ion or cupric ion	$CuCl_2$	Copper(II) chloride or cupric chloride

Among the transition metals, a few elements (zinc, silver, and cadmium) form only a single type of ion; they have a fixed ionic charge. Thus, they are *not* variable and *do not need* a Roman numeral in their names.

Zn^{2+} zinc ion Ag^+ silver ion Cd^{2+} cadmium ion

D. Ionic Compounds with Polyatomic Ions

A compound that consists of three or more kinds of atoms will contain a *polyatomic ion*. A polyatomic ion is a group of atoms with an overall charge. That charge, which is usually negative, is the result of adding electrons to a group of atoms to complete octets. The most common polyatomic ions consist of the nonmetals C, N, S, P, Cl, or Br combined with two to four oxygen atoms. Some examples are given in Table 3. The ions are named by replacing the ending of the nonmetal with *ate* or *ite*. The *ite* ending has one oxygen less than the most common form of the ion, which has an *ate* ending. Ammonium ion, NH_4^+, is positive because its group of atoms lost one electron.

Table 3 *Some Polyatomic Ions*

Common Polyatomic Ion		One Oxygen Less	
NH_4^+	ammonium ion		
OH^-	hydroxide ion		
NO_3^-	nitrate ion	NO_2^-	nitrite ion
CO_3^{2-}	carbonate ion		
HCO_3^-	bicarbonate ion (hydrogen carbonate ion)		
SO_4^{2-}	sulfate ion	SO_3^{2-}	sulfite ion
HSO_4^-	bisulfate ion (hydrogen sulfate ion)	HSO_3^-	bisulfite ion (hydrogen sulfite ion)
PO_4^{3-}	phosphate ion	PO_3^{3-}	phosphite ion

To write a formula with a polyatomic ion, we determine the ions needed for charge balance just as we did with the simple ions. When two or more polyatomic ions are needed, the formula of the ion is enclosed in parentheses and the subscript placed *outside*. *No change is ever made in the formula of the polyatomic ion itself.* Consider the formula of the compound formed by Ca^{2+} and NO_3^- ions.

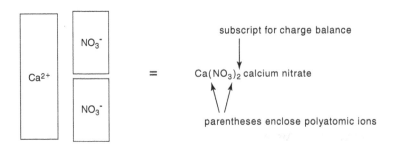

E. Covalent (Molecular) Compounds

Covalent bonds form between two nonmetals found in Groups 4, 5, 6, or 7 or H. In a *covalent compound,* octets are achieved by sharing electrons between atoms. The sharing of one pair of electrons is called a single bond. A double bond is the sharing of two pairs of electrons between atoms. In a triple bond, three pairs of electrons are shared. To write the formula of a covalent compound, determine the number of electrons needed to complete an octet. For example, nitrogen in Group 5 has five valence electrons. Nitrogen atoms need three more electrons for an octet; they share three electrons.

Electron-Dot Structures

The formulas of covalent compounds are determined by sharing the valence electrons until each atom has an octet. For example, in water (H_2O), oxygen shares two electrons with two hydrogen atoms. Oxygen has an octet and hydrogen is stable because it has two electrons in the first valence shell.

Dot Structure for H_2O

In another example, we look at a compound, CO_2, that has double bonds. In the elements' electron-dot structures, carbon has 4 valence electrons and each oxygen atom has 6. Thus a total of 16 (4 + 6 + 6) electrons can be used in forming the octets by sharing electrons. We can use the following steps to determine the electron-dot structure for CO_2:

1. Connect the atoms with pairs of electrons, thus using 4 electrons.

    O $\vdots$ C $\vdots$ O

2. Place the remaining 12 electrons (16 − 4) around the atoms. Don't add more electrons.

    $\vdots$ O $\vdots$ C $\vdots$ O $\vdots$

3. If octets *cannot* be completed, try sharing more electrons. In step 2, the octets are complete for the oxygen atoms, but not for the carbon. One pair of electrons from each oxygen atom is moved to share with carbon. Now all the atoms have octets. There are still 16 electrons used, but they are now arranged to give each atom an octet. There are two double bonds in the CO_2 molecule.

sharing two pairs of electrons makes double bonds

Names of Covalent Compounds

Binary (two-element) covalent compounds are named by using *prefixes* that give the number of atoms of each element in the compound. The first nonmetal is named by the element name; the second ends in *ide*. The prefixes are derived from the Greek names: mono (1), di (2), tri (3), tetra (4), penta (5), hexa (6), hepta (7), and octa (8). Usually the prefix *mono* is not shown for the first element. See Table 4.

Table 4 *Some Formulas and Names of Covalent Compounds*

Formula	Name
CO	carbon **mono**xide
CO_2	carbon **di**oxide
PCl_3	phosphorus **tri**chloride
N_2O_4	**di**nitrogen **tetr**oxide (drop *a* in a double vowel)
SCl_6	sulfur **hexa**chloride

F. Electron Dot Structures and Molecular Shape

A molecule has a shape such as linear, bent, trigonal planar, pyramidal, or tetrahedral. The electron-pair repulsion (VSEPR) model indicates that the bond angles in a molecule are determined when the valence electrons in bonds and lone pairs move as far apart as possible. Counting the groups of electrons that are shared pairs and lone pairs determines the electron geometry and bond angle. Atoms attached to the groups of electrons determine the molecular geometry. See Table 5.

Table 5 *Molecular Geometry for Atoms*

Total electron groups	Shared pairs	Lone pairs	Electron geometry	Bond angle	Molecular geometry	Examples
2	2	0	linear	180°	linear	$BeCl_2$, CO_2
3	3	0	trigonal planar	120°	trigonal planar	BF_3
3	2	1	trigonal planar	120°	bent	SO_2
4	4	0	tetrahedral	109°	tetrahedral	CH_4, CCl_4
4	3	1	tetrahedral	109°	pyramidal	NH_3
4	2	2	tetrahedral	109°	bent	H_2O

Polar and Nonpolar Molecules

When there is a difference of 0.4 or more between the electronegativity of the central atom and an attached atom, the bond is polar. If the polar bonds in a molecule are symmetrical and the dipoles cancel, the molecule itself is nonpolar. When the dipoles do not cancel, the molecule is polar.

Lab Information

Time: 2–3 hr

Comments: Tear out the report sheets and place them beside the matching procedures.

Related Topics: Ions, ionic bonds, naming ionic compounds, covalent bond, covalent compounds, naming covalent compounds

Experimental Procedures    GOGGLES REQUIRED!

A.   Electron-Dot Structures

Write the electron arrangements for atoms and their ions. Determine the number of electrons lost or gained and write the electron-dot structure of the ion that each would form along with its symbol, ionic charge, and name.

B.   Ionic Compounds and Formulas

   Materials: Reference books: *Merck Index* or *CRC Handbook of Chemistry and Physics,* display of compounds

B.1   **Physical properties** In the laboratory display of compounds observe NaCl, sodium chloride. Describe its appearance. Using a chemistry reference such as the *Merck Index* or the *CRC Handbook of Chemistry and Physics,* record the density and melting point.

B.2   **Formulas of ionic compounds** Use the periodic table to write the positive and negative ion in each compound. Use charge balance (net total = zero) to write the correct formula. Use subscripts when two or more ions are needed.

B.3   **Names of ionic compounds** From the formula of each ionic compound, write the compound name by placing the metal name first, then the nonmetal name ending in *ide.*

C.   Ionic Compounds with Transition Metals

C.1   **Physical properties** In the display of compounds observe $FeCl_3$, iron(III) chloride or ferric chloride. Describe its appearance. Using a chemistry reference such as the *Merck Index* or the *CRC Handbook of Chemistry and Physics,* record the density and melting point.

C.2   **Formulas of ionic compounds** Use the periodic table to write the positive and negative ion in each compound. Use charge balance (net total = zero) to write the correct formula. Use subscripts when two or more ions are needed.

C.3   **Names of ionic compounds** From the formula of each ionic compound, write the compound name by placing the metal name first, then the nonmetal name ending in *ide.* Be sure to indicate the ionic charge if the transition metal has a variable valence by using a Roman numeral or using the *ous* or *ic* ending.

D.   Ionic Compounds with Polyatomic Ions

D.1   **Physical properties** In the display of compounds observe K_2CO_3, potassium carbonate. Describe its appearance. Using a chemistry reference book such as the *Merck Index* or the *CRC Handbook of Chemistry and Physics,* record the density and melting point.

D.2   **Formulas of ionic compounds** Use the periodic table to write the positive and negative (polyatomic) ion in each compound. Use charge balance (net total = zero) to write the correct formula. Use subscripts when two or more ions are needed. Use parentheses when two or more polyatomic ions are needed for charge balance.

D.3   **Names of ionic compounds** Name the compounds listed, using the correct names of the polyatomic ions.

E. Covalent (Molecular) Compounds

E.1 **Electron-dot formulas of elements** Write the electron-dot structure for each nonmetal.

E.2 **Physical properties** In the display of compounds observe water, H_2O. Describe its appearance. Using a chemistry reference such as the *Merck Index* or the *CRC Handbook of Chemistry and Physics,* record the density and melting point.

E.3 **Electron-dot structures** Write the electron-dot structure for each covalent compound. Name each compound, using prefixes to indicate the number of atoms of each element. By convention, the prefix *mono* can be omitted from the name of the first nonmetal.

F. Electron Dot Structures and Molecular Shape

Obtain a molecular model set and build a model of each of the molecules or ions listed in the report sheet.

Complete the following for each of the molecules or polyatomic ions listed in the report page.

1. Draw the electron dot structure.

2. Count the electron groups around the central atom.

3. Use VSEPR to determine the electron geometry.

4. Determine the bond angle.

5. Count the numbers of atoms bonded to the central atom.

6. Use the number of bonded atoms to identify the molecular geometry.

7. Indicate if the molecules listed would be polar or nonpolar.

Report Sheet

Date _____   Name _____

Section _____   Team _____

Instructor _____   _____

Pre-Lab Study Questions

1. Where are the valence electrons in an atom?

2. How are positive and negative ions formed?

3. How do subscripts represent the charge balance of ions?

4. Why are electrons shared in covalent compounds?

5. How do the names of covalent compounds differ from the names of ionic compounds?

6. What are polyatomic ions?

7. How does the number of electron pairs around a central atom determine its shape?

Report Sheet

A. Electron-Dot Structures

Element	Atomic Number	Electron Arrangement of Atom	Electron-Dot Structure	Loss or Gain of Electrons	Electron Arrangement of Ion	Ionic Charge	Symbol of Ion	Name of Ion
Sodium	11	2-8-1	Na•	lose $1e^-$	2-8	1+	Na^+	sodium ion
Nitrogen	7	2-5	•N• (with dots)	gain $3e^-$	2-8	3–	N^{3-}	nitride ion
Aluminum								
Chlorine								
Calcium								
Oxygen								

Report Sheet

B.   Ionic Compounds and Formulas

B.1   **Physical properties**

Compound	Appearance	Density	Melting Point

B.2   **Formulas of ionic compounds**

Name	Positive Ion	Negative Ion	Formula
Sodium chloride	Na^+	Cl^-	
Magnesium chloride			
Calcium oxide			
Lithium phosphide			
Aluminum sulfide			
Calcium nitride			

B.3   **Names of ionic compounds**

K_2S	Potassium sulfide
BaF_2	
MgO	
Na_3N	
$AlCl_3$	
Mg_3P_2	

Report Sheet

C.   Ionic Compounds with Transition Metals

C.1   **Physical properties**

Compound	Appearance	Density	Melting Point

C.2   **Formulas of ionic compounds**

Name	Positive Ion	Negative Ion	Formula
Iron(III) chloride	Fe^{3+}	Cl^-	
Iron(II) oxide			
Copper(I) sulfide			
Copper(II) nitride			
Zinc oxide			
Silver sulfide			

C.3   **Names of ionic compounds**

Cu_2S	Copper(I) sulfide
Fe_2O_3	
$CuCl_2$	
FeS	
Ag_2O	
$FeBr_2$	

D.   Ionic Compounds with Polyatomic Ions

D.1   **Physical properties**

Compound	Appearance	Density	Melting Point

Report Sheet

D.2 **Formulas of ionic compounds**

Name	Positive Ion	Negative Ion	Formula
Potassium carbonate	K^+	CO_3^{2-}	
Sodium nitrate			
Calcium bicarbonate			
Aluminum hydroxide			
Lithium phosphate			
Potassium sulfate			

D.3 **Names of ionic compounds**

$CaSO_4$	Calcium sulfate
$Al(NO_3)_3$	
Na_2CO_3	
$MgSO_3$	
$Cu(OH)_2$	
$Mg_3(PO_4)_2$	

Questions and Problems

Q.1 Write the correct formulas for the following ions:

sodium ion _____   oxide ion _____   calcium ion _____

chloride ion _____   sulfate ion _____   iron(II) ion _____

E.   Covalent (Molecular) Compounds

E.1 **Electron-dot formulas of elements**

Hydrogen	Carbon	Nitrogen	Oxygen	Sulfur	Chlorine
H$^\bullet$					

Report Sheet

E.2 Physical properties

Compound	Appearance	Density	Melting Point

E.3 Electron-dot structures

Compound	Electron-Dot Structure	Name
H_2O		
SBr_2		
PCl_3		
CBr_4		
SO_3		

Questions and Problems

Q.2 a. Identify each of the following compounds as ionic or covalent.
  b. Write the correct formula for each.

	Ionic/Covalent	Formula
sodium oxide	_____	_____
iron(III) bromide	_____	_____
sodium carbonate	_____	_____
carbon tetrachloride	_____	_____
nitrogen tribromide	_____	_____

Report Sheet

F. Electron Dot Structures and Molecular Shape

Formula	1. Electron dot Structure	2. Total number of electron groups	3. Electron geometry	4. Bond angle	5. Number of bonded atoms	6. Molecular geometry	7. Polar or nonpolar?
H_2O							
SBr_2							
NCl_3							
CBr_4							
SO_3							
CO_2							
NO_3^-							
$CHCl_3$							

Goals

- Distinguish between a calorie, kilocalorie, and nutritional Calorie.
- Use the specific heat of water to calculate heat lost or gained.
- Calculate the specific heat in cal/g °C and J/g °C of a metal object.
- Calculate the caloric values of foods in kcal/g to calculate the kilocalories in a serving of food.
- Use nutrition data on food products to determine the kilocalories in one serving.

Discussion

A. Specific Heat of a Metal

Every substance has the capacity to absorb heat. When heat is added to a substance, the temperature of that substance increases. Different substances vary in the amount of heat required to raise their temperatures by 1°C. **Specific heat** is the amount of heat in calories or joules that raises the temperature of 1 g of a substance by 1°C.

$$\text{Specific heat} = \frac{\text{Amount of heat (cal or J)}}{\text{Mass(g)} \times \text{change in temperature } \Delta T \text{ (°C)}}$$

Water has a very large specific heat, 1.00 cal/g °C or 4.18 J/g °C, compared to most substances. Water requires more heat than other substances before its temperature increases by 1°C. Because the specific heat of a substance is unique for that substance, specific heat can be used to identify a particular substance.

Table 1 Specific Heat Values for Selected Substances		
Substance	Specific Heat	
	cal/g °C	J/g °C
Water, H_2O (liquid)	1.00	4.18
Iron	0.11	0.46
Copper	0.093	0.39
Aluminum	0.22	0.92
Lead	0.031	0.13

From *Laboratory Manual for General, Organic, & Biological Chemistry,* Karen C. Timberlake. Copyright © 2002 Pearson Education, Inc., publishing as Benjamin Cummings. All rights reserved.

In this experiment, an insulated Styrofoam cup is used as a calorimeter (Figure 1). A measured amount of water is placed in the cup. After a metal is heated to the temperature of boiling water (about 100°C), it is quickly transferred to the water in the calorimeter. The heat lost by the hot metal is used to warm the water. As the temperature of the water increases, the temperature of the metal decreases until both the water and the metal reach the same final temperature. By measuring the increase in the temperature of the water, we can calculate the amount of heat (calories or joules) given off by the hot metal.

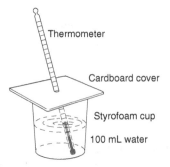

Thermometer

Cardboard cover

Styrofoam cup

100 mL water

Figure 1 A calorimeter consists of a Styrofoam cup(s), cover, water, and a thermometer

For example, suppose 100. g of water in the Styrofoam cup has an initial temperature of 24.5°C, and a final temperature of 27.0°C. The specific of water is 1.00 cal/g °C and the temperature change is 2.5°C (27.0°C – 24.5°C).

Step 1: Calculate the heat gain for the water

Heat (cal)   = g x ΔT (°C) x specific heat

Heat (cal)   = 100. g x 2.5°C x 1.00 cal/g °C

              = 250 cal

Because the heat gained by the water sample is equal to the heat lost by the metal, we know that the metal lost 250 calories of heat. If the boiling water that heated the metal had a temperature of 100.0°C, the temperature change for the metal is 73.0°C (100.0 – 27.0°C). Using the heat loss of the metal, and a mass (g) of the metal of 32.3 g, and the decrease in the temperature of the metal, we can calculate the specific heat of that metal.

Step 2: Calculate the specific heat of the metal.

$$\text{Specific heat (metal)} = \frac{\text{cal}}{\text{Mass (g) x } \Delta T \text{ (°C)}} = \frac{250 \text{ cal}}{(32.3 \text{ g})(73.0°C)}$$

$$= 0.11 \text{ cal/g°C}$$

The metal is probably iron because the experimental result matches the known specific heat of iron.

B. Measuring the Caloric Value of a Food

The calories in a sample of food are measured in the laboratory using a calorimeter. In this lab, you will use a simple setup to illustrate how the calories in a sample of food can be determined. Burning a cheese puff or some chips releases heat that is used to heat water in an aluminum can. In our setup, some of the heat is lost to the can and the surrounding air. However, you can get an idea of how nutritionists determine the caloric content of foods. Food calories are usually given as kilocalories (Calories). Caloric values for foods are reported as kcal/g of food.

C. Food Calories

Our diets contain foods that provide us with energy. We need energy to make our muscles work, to breathe, to synthesize molecules in the body such as protein and fats, and to repair tissues. A typical diet required by a 25-year-old woman is about 2000–2500 kcal. By contrast a bicycle rider has a higher energy requirement and needs a diet that provides 4000 kcal. The nutritional energy of food is determined in Calories (Cal), which are the same as 1000 cal or 1 kilocalorie.

Nutritionists use calorimeters to establish the caloric values for the three food types: carbohydrates, 4 kcal/g; fats, 9 kcal/g; and proteins, 4 kcal/g. By measuring the amount of each food type in a serving, the kilocalories can be calculated. For example, a candy that is composed of 12 g of carbohydrate will provide 48 kcal. Usually the values are rounded to the nearest tens place.

$$12 \text{ g carbohydrate} \quad \times \quad \frac{4 \text{ kcal}}{1 \text{ g carbohydrate}} \qquad = 48 \text{ kcal or } 50 \text{ kcal}$$

Lab Information

Time:	2–3 hr
Comments:	Tear out the lab report sheets and place them beside the matching procedures. Be careful with boiling water.
Related topics:	Specific heat, measuring heat energy, calculating heat in calories and joules, nutritional calorie, caloric values.

Experimental Procedures   GOGGLES REQUIRED!

A. Specific Heat of a Metal

Materials: Thermometer, Bunsen burner, ring stand, iron ring, wire screen, 400-mL beaker, balance, calorimeter (Styrofoam cup and cover), stirring rod, and metal object

Fill the 400-mL beaker about two-thirds full of water. Place the beaker and water on a wire screen set on an iron ring so that the ring is about 6 cm above the top of the Bunsen burner. Light your Bunsen burner and begin heating the water in the beaker.

A.1 Obtain a metal object. Record any identification number for the metal. Using a balance, determine the mass of the metal object. Record. Tie a length of string or fishing line to the metal object and gently lower it into the water bath. Allow the water bath containing the metal object to boil for 10 minutes.

A.2 Obtain a Styrofoam cup and determine the mass of your calorimeter. Record.

A.3 Add about 50 mL of water to the Styrofoam cup (calorimeter) and determine the combined mass. Record. Note: There must be enough water to cover the metal object. If the metal object is large, you may need to place up to 100 mL of water in the Styrofoam cup.

A.4 After the water in the water bath has boiled for 10 minutes or more, use a thermometer to measure the temperature of the boiling water. Record. This is also the initial temperature of your metal object.

A.5 Measure the temperature of the water in your Styrofoam cup (calorimeter). Record.

A.6 Carefully remove the metal object from the text tube (boiling water bath) and quickly place the hot metal object in the water in the Styrofoam cup (calorimeter). Place the cover on top of the calorimeter, and use the thermometer or a stirring rod to gently stir. Be careful not to hit the metal object with the thermometer. The highest temperature reached will be the final temperature of both the water and the metal object. Record this temperature.

Dry off the metal object. If you are going to run a second trial, repeat the preceding procedures.

Calculations

A.7 Calculate the temperature change for the water in the Styrofoam calorimeter.
Temperature change for the water = Final temperature of water – initial temperature of water

A.8 Calculate the heat in calories that were transferred from the metal to heat the water.
$$cal = g \times \Delta T \, (°C) \times specific\ heat$$

A.9 State the number of calories lost by the metal object.
Heat (cal) lost by the metal = Heat (cal) gained by the water

A.10 Calculate the temperature change for the metal.
$\Delta T \, (°C)$ of metal =
Initial temperature of the metal (boiling water bath) – final temperature (metal and water)

A.11 Calculate the specific heat of the metal
$$Specific\ heat\ of\ the\ metal = \frac{amount\ of\ heat\ (calories)}{Mass\ of\ metal\ (g) \times temperature\ change\ (\Delta T\ °C)}$$

Calculate the specific heat of the metal in joules/g °C.

A.12 Use Table 8.1 to try to identify the type of metal in the object. Your instructor may add other values for identification.

B. Measuring the Caloric Value of a Food
This may be an instructor demonstration

> **Materials:** Aluminum can, food sample such as chips or cheese puffs, thermometer, two iron rings, a clamp, wire screen, Bunsen burner

B.1 Obtain an aluminum can and determine its mass. Add about 100 mL of water and determine the combined mass of the water and the can.

Set up in the hood: Place the can in an iron ring that holds it. Attach a second iron ring covered with a wire screen a short distance below the aluminum can. Suspend a thermometer from a clamp so that the bulb is below the water level in the aluminum can.

B.2 Weigh the food sample. Record.

B.3 Record the initial temperature of the water in the can. Place the food sample on the wire screen below the aluminum can. Ignite the food sample using a match or Bunsen burner. Remove the heat source immediately and let the food sample burn. Record the final (highest) temperature reached by the water in the can.

B.4 Weigh the ash and any remaining food sample. Record

Calculations

B.5 Calculate the mass of water in the aluminum can.

B.6 Calculate the temperature change of the water after it is heated by the combustion reaction of the burning food.

B.7 Calculate the heat gain of the water in the aluminum can in calories and kilocalories. This is also the heat lost by the food sample.

Heat (cal) = mass (g) water x ΔT (°C) x 1.00 cal/g °C

Kilocalories (Calories) = heat(cal) x 1 kcal/1000 cal

B.8 Calculate the mass of food sample that burned. Subtract the mass of ash and any remaining unburned food after combustion.

B.9 Calculate the caloric value of the food.

$$\text{Caloric value} \quad = \quad \frac{\text{kcal (Cal)}}{\text{Mass (g) of food sample burned}}$$

C. Food Calories

Materials: Food products with nutrition data on labels

C.1 Obtain a food product that has a Nutrition Facts label. Indicate the serving size.

C.2 List the grams of fat, carbohydrate, and protein in one serving of the food.

C.3 From the mass of each food type, calculate the Calories (kcal) of each food type in one serving using the accepted caloric values.

C.4 Determine the total Calories (kcal) in one serving.

C.5 Compare your total to the Calories listed on the upper portion of the label. Usually these totals are rounded to the nearest tens place.

Report Sheet

Date _____   Name _____

Section _____   Team _____

Instructor _____

Pre-Lab Study Questions

1. What is meant by the term specific heat?

2. Why is a measured amount of water needed to determine the specific heat of a metal object?

3. How is the caloric value (kcal/g) of a food sample determined?

A.   Specific Heat of a Metal

A.1   Identification Number _____

	First run	**Second run**
Mass of metal	_____	_____
A.2 Mass of Stryofoam calorimeter	_____	_____
A.3 Mass of Stryofoam calorimeter and water	_____	_____
A.4 Temperature of boiling water bath	_____	_____
A.5 Initial temperature of water in calorimeter	_____	_____
A.6 Final temperature of water and metal in calorimeter	_____	_____

Calculations

	First run	Second run
A.7 Temperature change ΔT (°C) for water	_____	_____
A.8 Heat calories used to warm water *(Show calculations)*	_____	_____
A.9 Heat calories lost by the metal object	_____	_____

Report Sheet

A.10 Temperature change ΔT (°C) for metal   _____   _____

A.11 Specific heat of the metal (cal/g °C)   _____   _____
      (Show calculations)

      Specific heat of the metal in joules/g °C   _____   _____

A.12 Type of metal   _____

Questions and Problems

Q.1 Why did you need to transfer the metal quickly from the hot water bath to the water in the Styrofoam cup calorimeter?

Q.2 Write the expression and value for the specific heat of water.

Q.3 Water has one of the largest specific heats of any substance. Why is this important for the human body?

Q.4 How many calories are required to raise the temperature of 225 g of water from 42°C to 75°C?

Q.5 A metal object with a mass of 19 g is heated to 96°C, then transferred to a calorimeter containing 75 g of water at 18°C. The water and metal object reach a final temperature of 22°C.

   a. What is the specific heat of this metal object?

   b. What is the metal?

Report Sheet

B. Measuring the Caloric Value of a Food

Type of Food sample   _____

B.1 Mass of aluminum can and water   _____

     Mass of aluminum can   _____

B.2 Mass of food   _____

B.3 Final temperature of water   _____

     Initial temperature of water   _____

B.4 Mass of food remaining   _____

Calculations

B.5 Mass of water   _____

B.6 Temperature change for water   _____

B.7 Heat gain (calories) of water   _____
     (Show calculations)

     Heat gain (kilocalories) of water   _____

     Heat loss (calories) of food sample   _____

     Heat loss (kilocalories) of food sample   _____

B.8 Mass of food undergoing combustion   _____

B.9 Caloric value (kcal/g) of food sample   _____
     Show calculations

Questions and Problems

Q.6 A 0.25 g sample of a pretzel is burned. The heat it gives off is used to heat 50. g of water from 18°C to 42°C. What is the caloric value of the pretzel in kcal/g?

Report Sheet

C. Food Calories

C.1 Name of food product _____ Serving size_____

C.2 Mass of food types in one serving

Carbohydrate _____ g   Fat_____ g   Protein _____ g

C.3 Calculations for kcal per serving
(Show calculations.)
Carbohydrate   _____ kcal (Cal)

Fat   _____ kcal (Cal)

Protein   _____ kcal (Cal)

C.4 Total Calories (kcal) per serving   _____ kcal (Cal)

C.5 Calories (for one serving) listed on the label   _____ Cal

Questions and Problems

Q.7 What percent (%) of the total Calories in your food product is from fat?

What percent (%) of the total Calories in your food product is from carbohydrate?

What percent (%) of the total Calories in your food product is from protein?

Q.8 How does your calculated number of Calories compare to the Calories listed on the label of the food product?

Goals

- Prepare a heating curve and a cooling curve.
- Use the specific heat of water to calculate heat lost or gained.
- Calculate the heat of fusion for water.

Discussion

A.   A Heating Curve for Water

The temperature of a substance indicates the kinetic energy (energy of motion) of its molecules. When water molecules gain heat energy, they move faster and the temperature rises. Eventually the water molecules gain sufficient energy to separate from the other liquid molecules. The liquid changes to a gas in a change of state called *boiling*. The change of state from liquid to gas is indicated when the water temperature becomes constant. It is more obvious when a graph is drawn of the temperature change of the substance that is heated. When a liquid boils, a horizontal line (*plateau*) appears on the graph, as shown in Figure 1. This constant temperature is called its *boiling point*.

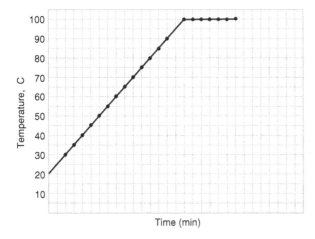

Figure 1   Example of a graph of a heating curve

B.   Graphing a Cooling Curve

When a liquid cools, its particles move more slowly. Attractions between the particles become so strong that they form a solid. This change of state is called freezing. There is no change in the temperature while the liquid is freezing. When the liquid reaches it freezing point, its temperature becomes constant. On the graph in Figure 2, the drop in temperature is shown. As the liquid cools, the temperature may drop temporary below its freezing point. But as it continues to freeze, you will notice a jump up in the temperature. This condition is called supercooling. The horizontal line or plateau that appears after the supercooling indicates the freezing point of the substance as it changes from a liquid to a solid.

From *Laboratory Manual for General, Organic, & Biological Chemistry*, Karen C. Timberlake. Copyright © 2002 Pearson Education, Inc., publishing as Benjamin Cummings. All rights reserved.

B. Graphing a Cooling Curve

Materials: The freezing-point apparatus, which consists of a large test tube containing a small amount of Salol (phenylsalicylate) and fitted with a two-hole stopper, thermometer, and wire stirrer. Do not try to pull out the stopper or thermometer. It is frozen in the Salol until heated. Hot-water bath: 400-mL beaker about $^1/_2$ full of water, Bunsen burner, iron ring, and wire screen

The substance called Salol is a solid at room temperature. Your instructor will indicate the location of the already prepared test tubes containing Salol and stirring apparatus. See Figure 4.

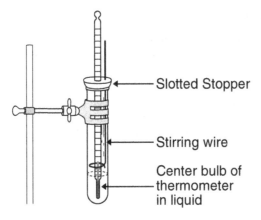

— Slotted Stopper

— Stirring wire

Center bulb of
thermometer
in liquid

Figure 4   Stirring apparatus for cooling curve and freezing point determination of Salol.

B.1   The Salol in the freezing-point apparatus must be melted before this experiment can begin. Prepare a hot water bath and place the test tube setup containing the Salol in the warm water. Let the temperature of the melted Salol go up to about 70°C *not to the boiling temperature of water*. All the Salol should now be liquid.

Turn off the Bunsen burner and remove the test tube with the Salol from the warm water. Clamp the test tube and contents to a ring stand. Gently raise and lower the wire stirrer to mix the contents. Each minute record the temperature as the liquid Salol cools. You will have to stop stirring when the stirrer becomes frozen in the Salol. After solid forms, take at least five more temperature readings. A constant temperature for five or more minutes indicates that the Salol has reached its freezing point. Return the freezing-point apparatus and contents to your instructor.

B.2   Plot the cooling curve for Salol on the graph provided in the report page. For a review of graphing, see page xviii in the preface of this lab manual. Label the areas of liquid state and solid state, super-cooling (if any), and the freezing point of the Salol.

C. Energy in Changes of State

Materials: Calorimeter (Styrofoam® cup and cardboard cover), thermometer, 50- or 100-mL graduated cylinder, 100-mL beaker, ice

C.1 Weigh an empty Styrofoam cup.

C.2 Add 100 mL of water to the cup and reweigh.

C.3 Record the initial temperature of the water in the calorimeter. See Figure 5. Add 2 or 3 ice cubes (or crushed ice that fills a 100-mL beaker) to the water in the cup. Stir strongly. Check the temperature of the ice water. Add ice until the temperature drops to 2–3°C. If some ice is not melted, remove it immediately. Record the final temperature of the water.

C.4 Weigh the Styrofoam (calorimetry) cup with the initial sample of water and the melted ice. The increase in mass indicates the amount of ice that melted.

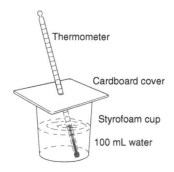

Thermometer

Cardboard cover

Styrofoam cup

100 mL water

Figure 5   Calorimetry setup with water, a thermometer, Styrofoam cup, and a cardboard cover

Calculations

C.5 Calculate the mass of water added to the Styrofoam cup.

C.6 Calculate the temperature change (ΔT) for the water.

C.7 Calculate the calories lost by the water.

Heat (cal) lost by water $=$ mass of water $\times \Delta T \times$ specific heat (1.00 cal/g °C)

This is the same number of calories that melted the ice.

C.8 Calculate the grams of ice that melted by subtracting the initial mass of the cup and water from the final mass of the cup and water after the ice melted.

C.9 Calculate your experimental value for the heat of fusion for ice.

$$\text{Heat of fusion (cal / g)} \; = \; \frac{\text{heat (cal) gained to melt ice}}{\text{grams of ice}}$$

Report Sheet

Date _____   Name _____

Section _____   Team _____

Instructor _____   _____

Pre-Lab Study Questions

1. Why is energy required for the heating or boiling process?

2. When water at 0°C freezes, is heat lost or gained?

A. A Heating Curve for Water

Volume of water: _____mL

A.1 Time (min)	Temperature (°C)	Time (min)	Temperature (°C)
0	_____	_____	_____
1	_____	_____	_____
2	_____	_____	_____
_____	_____	_____	_____
_____	_____	_____	_____
_____	_____	_____	_____
_____	_____	_____	_____
_____	_____	_____	_____
_____	_____	_____	_____
_____	_____	_____	_____

Report Sheet

A.2 Graphing the Heating Curve

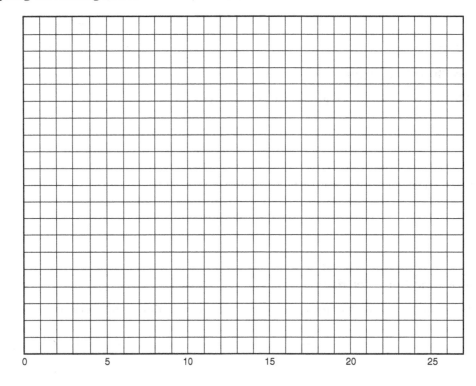

Time (min)

A.3 Boiling point of water   _____ °C

A.4 Temperature change (ΔT)   _____ °C

A.5 Volume of water   _____ mL

      Mass of water   _____ g

A.6 Number of calories needed to heat water   _____ cal
      (Show calculations.)

Questions and Problems

Q.1 On the heating curve, how long did it take for the temperature to rise to 60°C?

Report Sheet

B. Graphing a Cooling Curve

B.1

Time (min)	Temperature (°C)	Time (min)	Temperature (°C)
0	_____	_____	_____
1	_____	_____	_____
2	_____	_____	_____
3	_____	_____	_____
4	_____	_____	_____
5	_____	_____	_____
_____	_____	_____	_____
_____	_____	_____	_____
_____	_____	_____	_____
_____	_____	_____	_____
_____	_____	_____	_____

B.2 **Graphing the Cooling Curve**

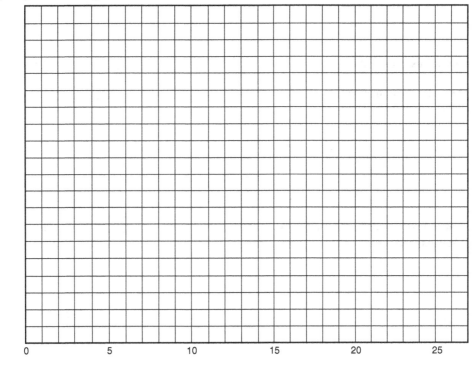

Time (min)

Questions and Problems

Q.2 What is the freezing point of Salol?

Report Sheet

C.   Energy in Changes of State

C.1   Empty calorimeter cup   _____ g

C.2   Calorimeter + water   _____ g

C.3   *Final* water temperature   _____ °C

     Initial water temperature   _____ °C

C.4   Calorimeter + water + melted ice   _____ g

Calculations

C.5   Mass of water   _____ g

C.6   Temperature change   _____ °C

C.7   Calories lost by water   _____ cal
     (Show calculations.)

     Calories used to melt ice   _____ cal

C.8   Mass of ice that melted   _____ g
     (Show calculations.)

C.9   Heat of fusion (calories to melt 1 g of ice)   _____ cal/g
     (Show calculations.)

Report Sheet

Questions and Problems

Q.3 When water is heated, the temperature eventually reaches a constant value and forms a plateau on the graph. What does the plateau indicate?

Q.4 175 g of water was heated from 15° to 88°C. How many kilocalories were absorbed by the water?

Q.5 How many calories are required at 0°C to melt an ice cube with a mass of 25 g?

Q.6 a. Calculate the amount of heat (kcal) released when 50.0 g of water at 100°C hits the skin and cools to a body temperature of 37°C.

b. Calculate the amount of heat (kcal) released when 50.0 g of steam at 100°C hits the skin, condenses, and cools to a body temperature of 37°C.

c. Use your answer in 6a and 6b to explain why steam burns are so severe.

Goals

- Observe physical and chemical properties associated with chemical changes.
- Give evidence for the occurrence of a chemical reaction.
- Write a balanced equation for a chemical reaction.
- Identify a reaction as a combination, decomposition, replacement, or combustion reaction.

Discussion

When a substance undergoes a physical change, it changes its appearance but not its composition. For example, when silver (Ag) melts and forms liquid silver (Ag), it undergoes a physical change from solid to liquid. In a chemical change, a substance is changed to give a new substance with a different composition and different properties. For example, when silver tarnishes, the shiny silver (Ag) changes to a dull-gray silver sulfide (Ag_2S), a new substance with different properties and a different composition. See Table 1.

Table 1 *Comparison of Physical and Chemical Changes*

Some Physical Changes	Some Chemical Changes
Change in state	Formation of a gas (bubbles)
Change in size	Formation of a solid (precipitates)
Tearing	Disappearance of a solid (dissolves)
Breaking	Change in color
Grinding	Heat is given off or absorbed

Balancing a Chemical Equation

In a chemical reaction, atoms in the reactants are rearranged to produce new combinations of atoms in the products. However, the total number of atoms of each element in the reactants is equal to the total number of atoms in the products. In an equation, the reactants are shown on the left and the products on the right. An arrow between them indicates that a chemical reaction takes place.

Reactants $\longrightarrow$ Products

To balance the number of atoms of each element on the left and right sides of the arrow, we write a number called a *coefficient* in front of the formula containing that particular element. Consider the balancing of the following unbalanced equation. The state of the substances as gas is shown as (*g*).

$N_2(g)$ + $H_2(g)$ $\longrightarrow$ $NH_3(g)$ *Unbalanced equation*

$N_2(g)$ + $H_2(g)$ $\longrightarrow$ $2NH_3(g)$ *A coefficient of 2 balances the N atoms.*

$N_2(g)$ + $3H_2(g)$ $\longrightarrow$ $2NH_3(g)$ *A coefficient of 3 balances the H atoms.*

The equation is now balanced.

Types of Reactions

There are many different chemical reactions, but most can be classified into the types of reactions shown in Table 2.

Table 2 *Common Types of Chemical Reactions*

Type of Reaction	Description	Example Equation
Combination	Elements or simple compounds form a more complex product.	$Cu + S \rightarrow CuS$
Decomposition	A reacting substance is split into simpler products.	$CaCO_3 \rightarrow CaO + CO_2$
Single replacement	One element takes the place of another element in a compound.	$Mg + 2HCl \rightarrow MgCl_2 + H_2$
Double replacement	Elements in two compounds switch places.	$AgNO_3 + NaCl \rightarrow AgCl + NaNO_3$
Combustion	Reactant and oxygen form an oxide product.	$S + O_2 \rightarrow SO_2$

Lab Information

Time: 2–2$^1/_2$ hr

Comments: Read all the directions and safety instructions carefully.

Match the labels on bottles and containers with the names of the substances you need.

Label your containers with the formulas of the chemicals you place in them.

Be sure that long hair is tied back.

A Bunsen burner is a potential hazard. Keep your work area clear of books, papers, backpacks, and other potentially flammable items.

Tear out the report sheets and place them beside the matching procedures.

Related Topics: Chemical change, chemical equation, balancing chemical equations

Experimental Procedures

 **GOGGLES REQUIRED!**

A. Magnesium and Oxygen

Materials: Magnesium ribbon (2–3 cm long), tongs, Bunsen burner

A.1 Obtain a small strip (2–3 cm) of magnesium ribbon. Record its appearance. Using a pair of tongs to hold the end of the magnesium ribbon, ignite it using the flame of a Bunsen burner. *As soon as the magnesium ribbon ignites, remove it from the flame. Shield your eyes as the ribbon burns.* Record your observations of the reaction and the physical properties of the product. Use complete sentences to describe your observations.

A.2 Balance the equation given for the reaction. Use 1 as a coefficient when one unit of that substance is required. The letters in parentheses indicate the physical state of the reactant or product: (*g*) gas, (*s*) solid. *Unbalanced equation:* Mg(*s*) + O$_2$(*g*) $\longrightarrow$ MgO(*s*)

A.3 Identify the type of reaction that has occurred. For this reaction, more than one reaction type may be used to classify the reaction.

B. Zinc and Copper(II) Sulfate

Materials: Two test tubes, test tube rack, 1 M $CuSO_4$ (copper(II) sulfate solution), $Zn(s)$

For all the experiments in parts C–F, use small quantities. For solids, use the amount of compound that will fit on the tip of a spatula or small scoop. Carefully pour small amounts of liquids into your own beakers and other containers. Measure out 3 mL of water in a test tube. Use this volume as a reference level for each of the experiments.

Do not place droppers or stirring rods into reagent bottles. They may contaminate a reagent for the entire class. Discard unused chemicals as indicated by your instructor.

B.1 Pour 3 mL (match the reference volume) of the *blue solution,* 1 M $CuSO_4$ (one molar copper(II) sulfate), into each of two test tubes. Obtain a small piece of zinc metal. Describe the appearance of the $CuSO_4$ solution and the small piece of zinc metal. Add the Zn metal piece to the $CuSO_4$ solution in one of the test tubes. The $CuSO_4$ solution in the other test tube is your reference for the initial solution color. Place the test tubes in your test tube rack and observe the color of the $CuSO_4$ solutions and the Zn piece again at 15 and 30 minutes. Pour the $CuSO_4$ solutions into the sink followed by a large amount of water. Rinse the piece of zinc with water and place it in a recycling container as directed by your instructor.

B.2 Balance the equation given for the reaction. The symbol *(aq)* means aqueous (dissolved in water).
Unbalanced equation: $Zn(s) + CuSO_4(aq) \longrightarrow Cu(s) + ZnSO_4(aq)$

B.3 Identify the type of reaction that has occurred.

C. Metals and HCl

Materials: Three test tubes, test tube rack, small pieces of $Cu(s)$, $Zn(s)$, and $Mg(s)$ metal
1 M HCl ***Caution: HCl is a corrosive acid. Handle carefully!***

C.1 Place 3 mL of 1 M HCl (match your reference volume from part C) in each of three test tubes. Describe the appearance of each metal. Carefully add a metal piece to the acid in each of the test tubes. Record any evidence of reaction such as bubbles of gas (H_2). Carefully pour off the acid and follow with large quantities of water to dilute. Rinse the metal pieces with water, dry, and return to your instructor.

C.2 Balance the equation given for each metal that gave a chemical reaction. If there was no reaction, cross out the products and write NR for no reaction.

Unbalanced equations: 1. $Cu(s) + HCl(aq) \longrightarrow CuCl_2(aq) + H_2(g)$

2. $Zn(s) + HCl(aq) \longrightarrow ZnCl_2(aq) + H_2(g)$

3. $Mg(s) + HCl(aq) \longrightarrow MgCl_2(aq) + H_2(g)$

C.3 Identify the type of reaction for each chemical reaction that occurred.

D. Reactions of Ionic Compounds

Materials: Three (3) test tubes, test tube rack
Dropper bottle sets of 0.1 M solutions: $CaCl_2$, Na_3PO_4, $BaCl_2$, Na_2SO_4, $FeCl_3$, KSCN

For each of these reactions, two substances will be mixed together. Describe your observations of the reactants before you mix them and then describe the products of the reaction. Look for changes in color, the formation of a solid (solution turns cloudy), the dissolving of a solid, and/or the formation of a gas (bubbling). Balance the equations for the reactions. Dispose of the solutions properly.

D.1 Place 20 drops each of 0.1 M $CaCl_2$ (calcium chloride) and 0.1 M Na_3PO_4 (sodium phosphate) into a test tube. Describe any changes that occur. Identify the type of reaction for each chemical reaction that occurred. *Unbalanced equation:* $CaCl_2(aq) + Na_3PO_4(aq) \longrightarrow Ca_3(PO_4)_2(s) + NaCl(aq)$

D.2 Place 20 drops each of 0.1 M $BaCl_2$ (barium chloride) and 0.1 M Na_2SO_4 (sodium sulfate) into a test tube. Describe any changes that occur. Identify the type of reaction for each chemical reaction that occurred. *Unbalanced equation:* $BaCl_2(aq) + Na_2SO_4(aq) \longrightarrow BaSO_4(s) + NaCl(aq)$

D.3 Place 20 drops each of 0.1 M $FeCl_3$ (iron(III) chloride) and 0.1 M KSCN (potassium thiocyanate) into a test tube. Describe any changes that occur. Identify the type of reaction for each chemical reaction that occurred. *Unbalanced equation:*

$$FeCl_3(aq) + KSCN(aq \longrightarrow Fe(SCN)_3(aq) + KCl(aq)$$

E. Sodium Carbonate and HCl

Materials: Test tube, test tube rack, 1 M HCl solution, $Na_2CO_3(s)$, and matches or wood splints

E.1 Place about 3 mL of 1 M HCl in a test tube. Add a small amount of solid Na_2CO_3 (about the size of a pea) to the test tube. Record your observations. ***Caution: HCl is corrosive. Clean up any spills immediately. If spilled on the skin, flood the area with water for at least 10 minutes.***

E.2 Identify the type of reaction for each chemical reaction that occurred. *Unbalanced equation:* $Na_2CO_3(s) + HCl(aq) \longrightarrow CO_2(g) + H_2O(l) + NaCl(aq)$

E.3 Light a match or wood splint and insert the flame inside the neck of the test tube. What happens to the flame? Record your observations.

Report Sheet

Date _____   Name _____

Section _____   Team _____

Instructor _____   _____

Pre-Lab Study Questions

1. Why is the freezing of water called a physical change?

2. Why are burning candles and rusting nails examples of chemical change?

3. What is included in a chemical equation?

4. How does a combination reaction differ from a decomposition reaction?

A. Magnesium and Oxygen

A.1 Initial appearance of Mg _____

_____

Observations of the reaction _____

_____

Appearance of the product _____

_____

A.2 Balance: _____ $Mg(s)$ + _____ $O_2(g)$ $\longrightarrow$ _____ $MgO(s)$

A.3 Type of reaction: _____

_____

77

Report Sheet

B. Zinc and Copper(II) Sulfate

B.1 Initially   Zn _____

CuSO$_4$ _____

15 min   Zn _____

CuSO$_4$ _____

30 min   Zn _____

CuSO$_4$ _____

B.2 Balance: ____ Zn(s) + ____CuSO$_4$(aq) $\longrightarrow$ ____Cu(s) + ____ ZnSO$_4$(aq)

B.3 Type of reaction: _____

_____

C. Metals and HCl

C.1 Observations

Cu   Initial: _____

Reaction: _____

Zn   Initial: _____

Reaction: _____

Mg   Initial: _____

Reaction: _____

C.2 Balance: ____Cu(s) + ____ HCl(aq) $\longrightarrow$ ____CuCl$_2$(aq) + ____ H$_2$(g)

____Zn(s) + ____ HCl(aq) $\longrightarrow$ ____ZnCl$_2$(aq) + ____ H$_2$(g)

____Mg(s) + ____ HCl(aq) $\longrightarrow$ ____MgCl$_2$(aq) + ____ H$_2$(g)

C.3 Type of reaction: Cu _____

Zn _____

Mg _____

Report Sheet

D.   Reactions of Ionic Compounds

D.1   **$CaCl_2$ and Na_3PO_4**

Observations:_____

_____

Type of reaction: _____

Balance: ____$CaCl_2(aq)$ + ____ $Na_3PO_4(aq)$ $\longrightarrow$ ____ $Ca_3(PO_4)_2(s)$ + ____ $NaCl(aq)$

D.2   **$BaCl_2$ and Na_2SO_4**

Observations:_____

_____

Type of reaction: _____

Balance: ____ $BaCl_2(aq)$ + ____ $Na_2SO_4(aq)$ $\longrightarrow$ ____ $BaSO_4(s)$ + ____ $NaCl(aq)$

D.3   **$FeCl_3$ and KSCN**

Observations:_____

_____

Type of reaction: _____

Balance: ____ $FeCl_3(aq)$ + ____ $KSCN(aq)$ $\longrightarrow$ ____ $Fe(SCN)_3(aq)$ + ____ $KCl(aq)$

E.   Sodium Carbonate and HCl

E.1   Observations:_____

_____

E.2   Type of reaction: _____

Balance: ____ $Na_2CO_3(s)$ + ____ $HCl(aq)$ $\longrightarrow$ ____ $CO_2(g)$ + ____ $H_2O(l)$ + ____ $NaCl(aq)$

E.3   Why did the flame of the burning match or splint go out?

Report Sheet

Questions and Problems

Q.1 What evidence of a chemical reaction might you see in the following cases?

   a. Dropping an Alka-Seltzer™ tablet into a glass of water

   _____

   b. Bleaching a stain

   _____

   c. Burning a match

   _____

   d. Rusting of an iron nail

   _____

Q.2 Balance the following equations:

   a. _____ $Mg(s)$ + _____ $HCl(aq)$ $\longrightarrow$ _____ $H_2(g)$ + _____ $MgCl_2(aq)$

   b. _____ $Al(s)$ + _____ $O_2(g)$ $\longrightarrow$ _____ $Al_2O_3(s)$

   c. _____ $Fe_2O_3(s)$ + _____ $H_2O(l)$ $\longrightarrow$ _____ $Fe(OH)_3(s)$

   d. _____ $Ca(OH)_2(aq)$ + _____ $HNO_3(aq)$ $\longrightarrow$ _____ $Ca(NO_3)_2(aq)$ + _____ $H_2O(l)$

Q.3 Write an equation for the following reactions. Remember that gases of elements such as oxygen are diatomic (O_2). Write the *correct formulas* of the reactants and products. Then correctly balance each equation.

   a. Potassium and oxygen gas react to form potassium oxide.

   b. Sodium and water react to form sodium hydroxide and hydrogen gas.

   c. Iron and oxygen gas react to form iron(III) oxide.

Report Sheet

Q.4 Classify each reaction as combination (C), decomposition (DC), single replacement (SR), or double replacement (DR).

a. $Ni + F_2 \longrightarrow NiF_2$ _____

b. $Fe_2O_3 + 3C \longrightarrow 2Fe + 3CO$ _____

c. $CaCO_3 \longrightarrow CaO + CO_2$ _____

d. $H_2SO_4 + 2KOH \longrightarrow K_2SO_4 + 2H_2O$ _____

Q.5 Predict what product(s) would form from the reaction of the following reactants:

a. $Zn + CuBr_2 \longrightarrow$ _____ + _____

b. $H_2 + Cl_2 \longrightarrow$ _____

c. $MgCO_3 \longrightarrow$ _____ + _____

d. $KCl + AgNO_3 \longrightarrow$ _____ + _____

Goals

- Identify a reaction as exothermic or endothermic.
- Identify the factors that affect the rate of a reaction.
- Observe that chemical reactions are reversible.
- Discuss factors that cause a shift in equilibrium.

Discussion

A. Exothermic and Endothermic Reactions

In an *exothermic* reaction, heat is released, which causes the temperature of the surroundings to increase. An *endothermic* reaction absorbs heat, which causes a drop in the temperature of the surroundings. Heat can be written as a product in an equation for an exothermic reaction and as a reactant in the equation for an endothermic reaction. Energy is required to break apart bonds and is released when bonds form. If energy is released by forming bonds, the reaction is exothermic. If energy is required to break apart bonds, the reaction is endothermic. In our cells, the bonds in carbohydrates are broken down to give us energy. Reactions that build molecules and repair cells are endothermic because they require energy.

Exothermic reactions: $C + O_2 \longrightarrow CO_2 + heat$

$$C_6H_{12}O_6 + 6O_2 \longrightarrow 6CO_2 + 6H_2O + energy$$
Glucose

Endothermic reactions: $Heat + PCl_5 \longrightarrow PCl_3 + Cl_2$

$$Energy + amino\ acids \longrightarrow protein$$

B. Rates of Reactions

The rate or speed at which a reaction occurs depends on the *amounts of the reactants*, the temperature, and the presence of a *catalyst*.

Amount of Reactants If more reactant is added, products form faster. For example, we normally breathe air that is 20% oxygen (O_2). However, if a person is given pure oxygen (100%), oxygenated hemoglobin (HbO_2) is formed faster.

$$Hb + O_2 \longrightarrow HbO_2$$

If some reactant is removed, the rate at which product forms is slowed. At higher altitudes the ability of hemoglobin to pick up O_2 is slowed because there is a lower amount of O_2. This results in less O_2 reaching the cells in the body and especially the brain. A lowered level of O_2 in the brain may result in mental confusion, hallucinations, and poor decisions, which has led to disastrous results for people who have tried to climb Mt. Everest and other high mountains without adequate sources of oxygen.

Temperature Typically a reaction goes at a faster rate as the temperature is increased. In general, the rate of a reaction doubles for a 10°C increase. We heat food to make it cook faster. When we have a fever, our metabolic reactions including our rate of breathing and our pulse go faster. In cardiac surgery, the body temperature is lowered to slow down the metabolic reactions and the amount of oxygen required by the brain.

In a chemical reaction, collisions between the reactants can lead to the formation of products. The energy that is needed to change the reactants into products is called the *energy of activation*. At high temperatures, more collisions have the energy to react and form products. At low temperature, few collisions lead to products.

Catalyst A typical catalyst increases the rate of a reaction without becoming a part of the product. Enzymes are biological catalysts that make components in our cells react at the rates required for cellular survival. Industry also makes use of catalysts. For example, the reaction of hydrogen with vegetable oils to produce margarine goes faster with a platinum (Pt) catalyst.

$$\text{Vegetable oil} + H_2 \xrightarrow{\text{Pt}} \text{margarine}$$

When a catalyst is present, the reaction can take an alternative pathway, which has a lower energy of activation. Then more reactants have the energy upon collision to change to products.

C. Reversible Reactions

When a reaction begins, reactants are converted to products. That means that the number of product atoms or molecules will increase and collisions will occur between the products. In some of the product collisions, bonds are broken and reactant particles re-formed. Thus, most reactions proceed in two directions—forward (reactants to products) and reverse (products back to reactants). In that case, the reaction is called a *reversible* reaction.

Eventually, the rate of the forward reaction becomes equal to the rate of the reverse reaction. There is no further change in the amounts of reactants and products and the system is at equilibrium. Some reversible reactions reach equilibrium quickly, but others may take a very long time. However, in any equilibrium, all of the reactants and products are present. For example, the reaction of ammonia (NH_3) and water produces ammonium ion (NH_4^+) and hydroxide ion (OH^-). At equilibrium, the products are always present along with the reactant molecules.

$$NH_3 + H_2O \rightleftharpoons NH_4^+ + OH^-$$

After this reversible reaction has reached equilibrium, any changes in the amounts of one of the reactants or products will create a stress. An increase in the amount of a reactant will favor the forward reaction. If a product is added, the reverse reaction will be favored. In a similar way, removal of reactants will shift the equilibrium in the reverse direction. Removing a product will favor the forward reaction.

D. Iron (III)-thiocyanate Equilibrium

In another reversible reaction the yellow Fe^{3+} ion and the colorless SCN^- (thiocyanate) ion, are in equilibrium with a deep red complex ion $FeSCN^{2+}$. More SCN^- forms $Fe(SCN)_2^+$.

$$\begin{array}{llll}
Fe^{3+} \text{ (aq)} & + \quad SCN^- \text{ (aq)} & \rightleftharpoons & FeSCN^{2+} \\
\text{yellow} & \quad\text{colorless} & & \text{red}
\end{array}$$

$$\begin{array}{llll}
Fe^{3+} \text{ (aq)} & + \quad 2\ SCN^- \text{ (aq)} & \rightleftharpoons & Fe(SCN)_2^+ \\
\text{yellow} & \quad\text{colorless} & & \text{red}
\end{array}$$

When the system contains mostly reactants, the solution is yellow. When the system shifts to products, the color changes to the deep red of $FeSCN^{2+}$.

When a system is at equilibrium, the rate of the forward reaction is equal to the rate of the reverse reaction. Then an *equilibrium constant* can be written, which represents the ratio of concentrations of the reactants and products.

$$K_{eq} = \frac{[products]}{[reactants]} = \frac{[FeSCN^{2+}]}{[Fe^{3+}][SCN^-]}$$

Visual colors allow us to see a shift in equilibrium between reactants and products. If we add more Fe^{3+} or SCN^-, the equilibrium shifts to product, which is red. If we add a substance that removes Fe^{3+} or SCN^-, the equilibrium shifts back to reactants. Then we will see the formation of the yellow color of the iron (III) ion.

One way to reduce the yellow color of Fe^{3+} is to add Cl^-, which forms a colorless $FeCl_4^-$ complex.

$$Fe^{3+} + 4\ Cl^- \rightleftharpoons FeCl_4^-$$
yellow   colorless

Lab Information

Time: 2– 2 ½ hr

Comments: Tear out the report sheets and place them next to the corresponding procedures. Carefully observe the colors and state of the components in the test tubes before and after reactions.

Related topics: Factors affecting rates of reactions, energy of activation, chemical equilibrium, factors affecting equilibrium

Experimental Procedures

Goggles are required!

A.   Exothermic and Endothermic Reactions

Materials: Two test tubes, test tube rack, water, scoop or spatula
$NH_4NO_3(s)$, anhydrous $CaCl_2(s)$, thermometer

A.1   Place 5 mL of water in each of two test tubes. Record the temperature of the water. Add one scoop of $NH_4NO_3(s)$ crystals to the water in the first test tube. Add one scoop of *anhydrous* $CaCl_2(s)$ to the water in the second test tube. *Anhydrous* means "without water." Stir each and record the temperature again.

$$NH_4NO_3(s) \xrightarrow{H_2O} NH_4^+(aq) + NO_3^-(aq)$$

$$CaCl_2(s) \xrightarrow{H_2O} Ca^{2+}(aq) + 2\ Cl^-(aq)$$

A.2 Describe each reaction as endothermic or exothermic.

A.3 To each equation, add the term heat on the side of the reactants (if endothermic) and on the side of the products (if exothermic).

B. Rates of Reactions

Materials: Test tubes, cleaned pieces of magnesium ribbon 2–3 cm long (about 0.4 g)
1.0 M HCl, 2.0 M HCl, 3.0 M HCl
Two 250-mL beakers, 400-mL beaker for hot water bath, ice
Vinegar (or 0.1 M HCl), $NaHCO_3$ (or baking soda or Alka-Seltzer), scoop or spatula, thermometer

B.1 **Amount of reactants** Obtain a piece of Mg and 10 mL of 1.0 M HCl. Place the Mg in a test tube. In this test you are going to measure the time required to completely dissolve the Mg. First note the time on a watch with a second hand or on a stopwatch. Then pour 10 mL of 1.0 M HCl solution into the test tube all at once. Stir. Record the amount of time for the Mg to completely react and disappear. At the end of the reaction determine whether the reaction is exothermic or endothermic by touching the bottom of the test tube.

Caution: HCl is an acid. Work carefully. If any HCl gets in your eyes wash immediately at the eye fountain.

Repeat the reaction of Mg and the other HCl solutions. Alternatively this work could be shared with other students. Record the time for each sample to completely react. Rank the rates of reactions from slowest to fastest.

Be sure to wash your hands at the end of this experiment.

B.2 **Temperature** Place 10 mL of vinegar (or 0.1 M HCl) in each of two large test tubes. Place one test tube in a 250-mL beaker half-filled with crushed ice. Cool to a temperature of 10°C or lower. Place the other test tube and vinegar in a 400-mL beaker about half-filled with water. Heat to 50–60°C. Remove the test tubes and place them in a test tube rack. Measure the temperature in each test tube. At the same time, add 1 scoop or 2 spatula tips of $NaHCO_3$ to each sample. Observe and compare the fizzing (bubbles) in each test tube. Determine which test tube clears first.

$$NaHCO_3 + H^+ \longrightarrow CO_2(g) + Na^+ + H_2O$$

C. Reversible Reactions

Materials: 3 test tubes, test tube rack, and droppers,
0.1 M $CuCl_2$, 0.1 M NaOH, 1 M NH_4OH, 0.1 M HCl or dropper bottle sets

The Cu^{2+} ion reacts with OH^- to form solid $Cu(OH)_2$, which is in equilibrium with the ions according to the following:

$$Cu(OH)_2(s) \rightleftharpoons Cu^{2+}(aq) + 2OH^-(aq)$$

Place 3 mL of 0.1 M $CuCl_2$ in each of three test tubes. To the first test tube add drops of 0.1 M NaOH until a white, cloudy precipitate of $Cu(OH)_2$ starts to form. Add the same number of drops to the other two test tubes containing $CuCl_2$ to give solid $Cu(OH)_2$.

C.1 **Test tube 1** Describe the initial appearance of the test tube. Using a dropper, add more 0.1 M NaOH, which increases the amount of OH⁻. Describe the change in the appearance of the sample in the test tube. In the equilibrium equation for $Cu(OH)_2$, identify the component that increased or decreased. Determine how the equilibrium shifted in response to this stress.

C.2 **Test tube 2** Describe the initial appearance of the test tube. Using a dropper, add drops of 1 M NH_4OH ($NH_3 + H_2O$). Describe the change of appearance of the sample in the test tube. NH_3 reacts with CU^{2+} to form the deep blue ion $Cu(NH_3)_4^{2+}$, which decreases the amount of Cu^{2+} in the equilibrium system for $Cu(OH)_2$.

$$Cu^{2+} + 4NH_3 \longrightarrow Cu(NH_3)_4^{2+}$$
$$\textit{deep blue}$$

In the equilibrium equation for $Cu(OH)_2$, identify the component that increased or decreased. Determine how the equilibrium shifted in response to this stress.

C.3 **Test tube 3** Using a dropper, add a few drops of 0.1 M HCl. Describe the change in the appearance of the sample in the test tube. H^+ from HCl reacts with the OH⁻ in the equilibrium system to form water, which decreases the amount of OH⁻.

$$H^+ + OH^- \longrightarrow H_2O$$

In the equilibrium equation for $Cu(OH)_2$, identify the component that increased or decreased. Determine how the equilibrium shifted in response to this stress.

D. Iron(III)-thiocyanate Equilibrium

Materials: 6 test tubes, test tube rack, small 100-mL beaker, 0.01 M $Fe(NO_3)_3$, 3 cork stoppers, 1 M $Fe(NO_3)_3$, 0.01 M KSCN, 1 M KSCN, 3 M HCl, 3 M NaOH, water, two 250-mL beakers, Bunsen burner, ice

Using a small beaker, prepare a stock equilibrium solution by mixing 10 mL of 0.01 M $Fe(NO_3)_3$ and 10 mL of 0.01 M KSCN.

D.1 Set up 6 test tubes in a test tube rack and label each. To each test tube, add 3 mL of the stock equilibrium solution. To tube 1 add 10 drops of water. The first test tube will be your control, which means that you compare its color to the colors that form in the other test tubes. No other reagents will be added to this control test tube. Record the color you observe in the control tube 1.

D.2 To tube 2, add slowly 10 drops of 1 M $Fe(NO_3)_3$. Place a cork stopper in the test tube and invert it several times to mix the contents. Record the color you observe in tube 2 and compare to tube 1.

D.3 To tube 3, add slowly 10 drops of 1 M KSCN. Place a cork stopper in the test tube and mix as before. Record the color you observe in tube 3 and any change in color.

D.4 To tube 4, add slowly 10 drops of 3 M HCl. Place a cork stopper in the test tube and mix as before. Record the color you observe in tube 4 and any change in color.

For the following, prepare a hot water bath by filling a 250-mL beaker about one half full of water and heating. Use a second 250-mL beaker as an ice bath by filling it about one half full with ice and water.

D.5 To tube 5, add slowly 10 drops of water and place the test tube in a beaker of warm water. Turn off the heat source to prevent the water from boiling. After 10 minutes, record the color you observe in tube 5 and any change in color.

D.6 To tube 6, add slowly 10 drops of water and place the test tube in a beaker of ice. After 10 minutes, record the color you observe in tube 6 and any change in color.

Report Sheet

Date _____   Name _____

Section _____   Team _____

Instructor _____

Pre-Lab Study Questions

1. How does an exothermic reaction differ from an endothermic reaction?

2. What factors increase the rate of a chemical reaction?

3. When is equilibrium established in a reversible reaction?

4. How does a system at equilibrium respond to the addition of more reactant? More product?

A.   Exothermic and Endothermic Reactions

A.1 NH_4NO_3 $CaCl_2$

    Initial temperature   _____   _____

    Final temperature   _____   _____

    Temperature change   _____   _____

A.2   Endothermic or exothermic   _____   _____

A.3   Equations (add *heat*)

$$NH_4NO_3(s) \xrightarrow{H_2O} NH_4^+(aq) + NO_3^-(aq)$$

$$CaCl_2(s) \xrightarrow{H_2O} Ca^{2+}(aq) + 2\,Cl^-(aq)$$

Report Sheet

Questions and Problems

Q.1 As a lab technician for a pharmaceutical company, you are responsible for preparing hot packs and cold packs. A hot pack involves the release of heat when a salt and water are mixed. A cold pack becomes colder because mixing a salt and water absorbs heat.

Which compound could you use to make a hot pack?

Which compound could you use to make a cold pack?

Q.2 When you burn a log in the fireplace or burn gasoline in a car, is the reaction (combustion) an endothermic or exothermic reaction?

B. Rates of Reactions

B.1 Amount of reactants

	Time (sec) for complete reaction	Exothermic or endothermic	Reaction rate from slowest to fastest
1.0 M HCl			
2.0 M HCl			
3.0 M HCl			

Questions and Problems

Q.3 How does the amount of reactant account for the differences in the rate of reaction?

Report Sheet

B.2 **Test Tube**   **Temperature**   **Observations**

1   _____   _____

_____

2   _____   _____

_____

Which test tube cleared first?   _____

Questions and Problems

Q.4 How does temperature affect the rate of a reaction?

C. Reversible Reactions

$$Cu(OH)_2(s) \rightleftharpoons Cu^{2+}(aq) + 2OH^-(aq)$$

Initial color of the $CuCl_2$ solution   _____

Color and appearance of $Cu(OH)_2(s)$ _____

	C.1 **Test tube 1**	C.2 **Test tube 2**	C.3 **Test tube 3**
Initial appearance			
Change in appearance			
What component in the equilibrium equation increased or decreased?			
Did the equilibrium shift to reactants or products?			

Report Sheet

Questions and Problems

Q.5 What is meant by the term *reversible* reaction?

Q.6 Explain how a change in the amount of a product causes a shift in equilibrium.

Q.7 Predict the direction that equilibrium will shift for each change in the components of the following reaction:

$$C(s) + H_2O(g) + \text{heat} \rightleftharpoons CO(g) + H_2(g)$$

a. Adding heat

b. Adding $CO(g)$

c. Removing $H_2(g)$

d. Adding $H_2O(g)$

Q.8 Write the equilibrium expression (K_{eq}) for the reaction:

$$PCl_5(g) \rightleftharpoons PCl_3(g) + Cl_2(g)$$

Report Sheet

D. Iron(III)-thiocyanate Equilibrium

	Test tube	Initial color	Final color	Ions that increase	Ions that decrease	Equilibrium shifted toward
D.1	1					
D.2	2					
D.3	3					
D.4	4					
D.5	5					
D.6	6					

Questions and Problems

Q. 9 Indicate whether the addition of each of the following increases or decreases the $FeSCN^{2+}$ in an equilibrium mixture. Explain.

Add	Increases $FeSCN^{2+}$	Decreases $FeSCN^{2+}$	Reason
a. Fe^{3+}			
b. Heat			
c. Cl^-			
d. Cooling			
e. SCN^-			

Soluble and Insoluble Salts

Goals

- Predict the formation of an insoluble salt.
- Observe the effect of temperature on solubility.
- Measure the solubility of KNO_3 at various temperatures, and graph a solubility curve.
- Test a variety of water samples for water hardness.
- Use water treatment techniques to purify water.

Discussion

A. Soluble and Insoluble Salts

Although many ionic compounds (salts) are soluble in water, some do not dissolve. They are known as insoluble salts. In medicine, the insoluble salt $BaSO_4$ is used as an opaque substance to help outline the gastrointestinal tract in x-ray images. Solubility rules are shown in Table 1.

Table 1 *Solubility Rules for Ionic Compounds*

Soluble in Water	Insoluble in Water
Any salt with Li^+, Na^+, K^+, NH_4^+, NO_3^-	
Most chlorides, Cl^-	$AgCl$, $PbCl_2$, and Hg_2Cl_2
Most sulfates, SO_4^{2-}	$BaSO_4$, $PbSO_4$, and $CaSO_4$
	Salts with OH^-, CO_3^{2-}, S^{2-}, PO_4^{3-}

When solutions of two ionic compounds are mixed, the formation of a solid indicates an insoluble salt. The positive ion of one substance and the negative ion of the other formed the insoluble salt. For example, mixing solutions of the soluble salts $NaCl$ and $AgNO_3$ will produce a white solid, which is the insoluble salt $AgCl(s)$.

$$AgNO_3(aq) + NaCl(aq) \longrightarrow AgCl(s) + NaNO_3(aq)$$
$$\text{Soluble salts} \qquad \text{Insoluble salt}$$

B. Solubility of KNO_3

When a solution holds the maximum amount of solute at a certain temperature, it is *saturated*. When more solute is added, the excess appears as a solid in the container. The maximum amount of solute that dissolves is called the *solubility* of that solute in that solvent. Solubility is usually stated as the number of grams of solute that dissolve in 100 mL (or 100 g) of water. The solubility depends upon several factors, including the nature of the solute and solvent, the temperature, and the pressure (for a gas). Most solids are more soluble in water at higher temperatures. Generally, the dissolving of a solid solute is endothermic, which means that solubility increases with an increase in temperature.

C. Testing the Hardness of Water

Hard water contains the ions Ca^{2+}, Mg^{2+}, and Fe^{3+}. When hard water reacts with soap, the ions in the hard water and some of the soap molecules form insoluble salts called soap scum. The soap molecules tied up in the scum are not free to perform their cleaning function. Initially soap is used to remove the ions, and then more soap is added to produce sudsing and cleaning. The reaction of a soap solution with the ions in hard water can be used to compare hardness of water samples.

D. Purification of Water

In water treatment plants, chemicals added to water will cause the formation of insoluble substances that sink to the bottom of the tank. The water on top is purified and can be drawn off for use.

Lab Information

Time: $2^1/_2$ hr
Comments: Tear out the Lab report sheets and place them beside the matching procedures.
Related Topics: Solubility, insoluble salts, saturated solution

Experimental Procedures   Wear your safety goggles!

A. Soluble and Insoluble Salts

Materials: Spot plate or transparency sheets
0.1 M solutions of NaCl, Na_2SO_4, $Ba(NO_3)_2$, $AgNO_3$, Na_3PO_4, $CaCl_2$, NaOH, Na_2CO_3
Droppers, or dropper bottles of the 0.1 M solutions

A.1 Write the ions that are in the two solutions used to form each of the mixtures listed.

A.2 Using the solubility rules, draw a circle around the ions that would form an insoluble salt.

A.3 Obtain a spot plate or a plastic sheet. Make mixtures by placing 2–3 drops of each solution in the same well or on the same spot on the plastic sheet. Look for the formation of a solid (insoluble salt). Record your observations.

A.4 Write the formula of the insoluble salts where solids were formed.

B. Solubility of KNO_3

Materials: Weighing paper or small container, spatula, stirring rod, large test tube, 400-mL beaker, buret clamp, hot plate or Bunsen burner, thermometer, 10-mL graduated cylinder, $KNO_3(s)$

To reduce the amount of KNO_3 used, each group of students will be assigned an amount of KNO_3 to weigh out. The results will be shared with the class.

B.1 Obtain a piece of weighing paper or a small container and weigh it carefully. (Or you may tare the container.)

B.2 Each group of students will be assigned an amount of KNO_3 from 2 to 7 grams. Weigh out an amount of KNO_3 that is close to your assigned amount. For example, if you are assigned an amount of 3 grams, measure out a mass such as 3.10 g or 3.25 g or 2.85 g. It is not necessary to add or remove KNO_3 to obtain exactly 3.00 g. Weigh carefully. Calculate the mass of KNO_3.

> *Taring a container on an electronic balance:* The mass of a container on an electronic balance can be set to 0 by pressing the tare bar. As a substance is added to the container, the mass shown on the readout is for the substance only. (When a container is *tared*, it is not necessary to subtract the mass of the beaker.)

B.3 *The temperature at which the KNO₃ is soluble is determined by heating and cooling the KNO₃ solution.* Place 5.0 mL of water in a large test tube. Add your weighed amount of KNO_3. Clamp the test tube to a ring stand and place the test tube in a beaker of water. Use a hot plate or Bunsen burner to heat the water. See Figure 1. Stir the mixture and continue heating until all the KNO_3 dissolves.

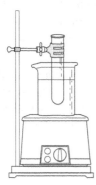

Figure 1   Heating the KNO_3 solution in a water bath

As soon as all the KNO_3 dissolves, turn off the burner or hot plate. Loosen the clamp and remove the test tube from the hot water. As the test tube and contents cool, stir gently with a thermometer. Look closely for the first appearance of crystals. As soon as you see some solid crystals, read the temperature of the solution. Record. This is the temperature at which the solution becomes saturated. The amount of KNO_3 in that solution is the solubility of KNO_3 at that temperature.

Place the test tube back into the hot water bath and begin heating again. Repeat the warming and cooling of the solution until you have obtained three or more temperature readings that agree. Set the test tube aside. In 15–20 minutes, observe the appearance of the crystals in the test tube.

To discard, add water and heat until the KNO_3 dissolves. Pour the solution in proper waste containers provided in the laboratory, *NOT* in the sink. (Solid KNO_3 can be recovered from the solution by evaporation to dryness.)

Calculations

B.4 Solubility is expressed as the number of grams of solute in 100 mL of water. Because you used a sample of 5.0 mL of water, the mass of the solute you measured out and the 5.0 mL of water are both multiplied by 20.

$$\frac{g\ KNO_3}{5.0\ mL\ water} \times \frac{20}{20} = \frac{g\ KNO_3}{100\ mL\ water} = \text{Solubility (g } KNO_3 \text{ per 100 mL water)}$$

Collect the solubility results of other KNO_3 solutions and their solubility temperatures from the other groups of students in the lab.

B.5 Prepare a graph of the solubility curve for KNO_3. Plot the solubility (g KNO_3/100 mL water) on the vertical axis and the temperature (0–100°C) on the horizontal axis.

C. Testing the Hardness of Water

Materials: 250-mL beaker, 50-mL (or 25-mL) graduated cylinder, two 250-mL flasks with stoppers, soap solution (dropper bottles), water samples

C.1   Place 50 mL of the water sample you are going to test (begin with distilled water) in a 250-mL flask. Add 1 drop of the soap solution. Stopper the flask and shake for 10 sec. With distilled water, you should see a thick layer of suds. If you don't, add another drop of soap solution and shake for 10 sec again. The suds that form in the distilled water sample will serve as your reference sample. Save for comparison. Shake again if necessary.

Add 1 drop of soap solution to another water sample. Shake. If no suds form, add drops of soap solution until the sample forms an amount of suds similar to that in the distilled water sample. Stop if no suds are formed after you have added 20 drops of soap solution. Test an assortment of water samples available in the lab or from your home, pool, or well. Record the number of drops required to soften each water sample.

D. Purification of Water

Materials: Test tubes, rack, muddy water, 1% $Al_2(SO_4)_3$, 1% Na_2SO_4, 1% NaCl

At water treatment plants, adding chemicals that cause the formation of large particles that sink to the bottom can purify hard water or wastewater. Such a process occurs in the settling tanks at a water filtration facility.

Set up four test tubes in a test tube rack. To each, add 10 mL of muddy water. Add the following chemicals, one to each test tube of the muddy water; label each.

(1) 5 mL water (control)   (3) 5 mL 1% $Al_2(SO_4)_3$

(2) 5 mL 1% NaCl   (4) 5 mL 1% Na_2SO_4

Stir each test tube thoroughly. Then allow the test tubes to stand undisturbed. Look for a separation of a precipitate and a clarification of the upper portion of water. Record your observations after 15, 30, and 45 minutes.

NS   no settling, still muddy   MS mostly settled, slightly cloudy

BS   beginning to settle, still murky   SC   settled, clear

SS   some settling, cloudy

Report Sheet

Date _____ Name _____

Section _____ Team _____

Instructor _____

Pre-Lab Study Questions

1. What is an insoluble salt?

A. Soluble and Insoluble Salts

Compounds in Mixture	A.1, A.2 Ions	A.3 Observations	A.4 Formula of Insoluble Salt (if any)
$AgNO_3$ + NaCl	Ag^+ NO_3^- Na^+ Cl^-		
$AgNO_3$ + Na_2SO_4			
$AgNO_3$ + Na_3PO_4			
$Ba(NO_3)_2$ + Na_2SO_4			
$CaCl_2$ + NaOH			
$CaCl_2$ + Na_2SO_4			
$CaCl_2$ + Na_2CO_3			

Questions and Problems

Q.1 Why do some mixtures of ionic compounds form a solid precipitate?

Report Sheet

B. Solubility of KNO₃

B.1 Mass of Container	B.2 Mass of Container + KNO₃	Mass of KNO₃	B.3 Temperature (Crystals Appear)	B.4 Solubility (g KNO₃/100 mL H₂O)

B.5 **Graphing the solubility of KNO₃ vs. temperature (°C)**

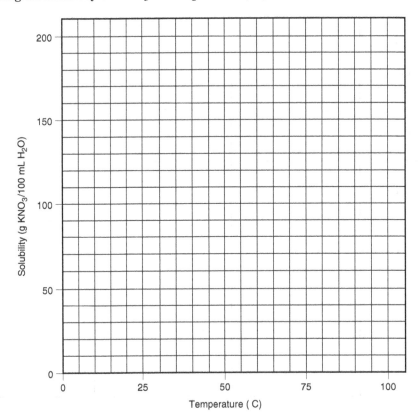

According to your graph, what is the effect of increasing temperature on the solubility of KNO₃?

Report Sheet

Questions and Problems

Q.2 The solubility of sucrose (common table sugar) at 70°C is 320 g/100 g H_2O.
a. How much sucrose can dissolve in 200 g of water at 70°C?

b. Will 400 g of sucrose dissolve in a teapot that contains 200 g of water at 70°C? Explain.

C.   Testing the Hardness of Water

C.1

Type of Water	Drops of Soap	Type of Water	Drops of Soap
distilled water	_____	mineral water	_____
tap water	_____	seawater	_____
_____	_____	_____	_____
_____	_____	_____	_____
_____	_____	_____	_____
_____	_____	_____	_____

Questions and Problems

Q.3 Which water sample was the hardest? Why?

Report Sheet

D. Purification of Water

Agent Added	15 Minutes	30 Minutes	45 Minutes
H_2O			
NaCI			
$Al_2(sO_4)_3$			
Na_2SO_4			

Questions and Problems

Q.4 Which chemical produced the most rapid settling? Why?

Goals

- Determine the presence of a cation or anion by a chemical reaction.
- Determine the presence of some cations and anions in an unknown salt.

Discussion

Solutions such as milk, coffee, tea, and orange juice contain an assortment of ions. In chemical reactions, these ions give a distinctive flame test, undergo color changes, or form a gas or an insoluble solid. Your observations of the results of a test are the key to identifying those same ions when you test unknown solutions. After you look at a test that produces some change when a particular ion reacts, you will look for the same change in an unknown sample. If the test result is the same, you assume that the ion is present in the unknown. If the test result does not occur then the ion is not in the unknown: the test is negative.

A. Tests for Positive Ions (Cations)

In this experiment, you will observe the tests for the following cations:

Cations	Solution
sodium (Na^+)	0.1 M NaCl
potassium (K^+)	0.1 M KCl
calcium (Ca^{2+})	0.1 M $CaCl_2$
iron (Fe^{3+})	0.1 M $FeCl_3$
ammonium (NH_4^+)	0.1 M NH_4Cl

The presence of Na^+, K^+, and Ca^{2+} is determined by the distinctive color the ions give in flame tests. The calcium ion also reacts with ammonium oxalate, $(NH_4)_2C_2O_4$, to give a white precipitate. When NH_4^+ is converted to ammonia (NH_3), a distinctive odor is emitted, and the fumes turn red litmus paper to blue. Iron (Fe^{3+}) is detected by the distinctive red color it gives with potassium thiocyanate, KSCN.

B. Tests for Negative Ions (Anions)

In this experiment, you will observe the tests for the following anions:

Anions	Solution
chloride (Cl^-)	0.1 M NaCl
phosphate (PO_4^{3-})	0.1 M Na_3PO_4
sulfate (SO_4^{2-})	0.1 M Na_2SO_4
carbonate (CO_3^{2-})	0.1 M Na_2CO_3

When $AgNO_3$ is added to the solutions to be tested for anions, several insoluble salts form. However, when nitric acid, HNO_3, is added to these precipitates, all the solids except AgCl will dissolve; the insoluble salt AgCl will remain in the test tube. Phosphate ion (PO_4^{3-}) reacts with ammonium molybdate and forms a yellow solid. When barium chloride, $BaCl_2$, is added to a solution containing SO_4^{2-}, a precipitate of $BaSO_4$ forms. Barium may form insoluble salts with some other anions, but the addition of HNO_3 dissolves all barium salts except $BaSO_4$. The insoluble $BaSO_4$ remains in the test tube after HNO_3 is added. Carbonate anion (CO_3^{2-}) is identified by adding HCl, which produces bubbles of CO_2 gas.

From *Laboratory Manual for General, Organic, & Biological Chemistry,* Karen C. Timberlake. Copyright © 2002 Pearson Education, Inc., publishing as Benjamin Cummings. All rights reserved.

C. Writing the Formula of Your Unknown Salt

As you proceed, you will test known solutions that contain a particular ion. Each student will receive an unknown sample containing a cation and an anion. After you observe reactions of knowns, you will carry out the same tests with your unknown. Therefore, you should expect to see a test that matches the reactions of one of the cations, and another for one of the anions. By identifying the ions in your unknown, you will be able to write the name and formula of your unknown salt.

D. Testing Consumer Products for Some Cations and Anions

Consumer products contain many of the same ions that you will test for in the experiment. Once you have gone through the procedures and identified positive test results for cations and anions, the same procedures can be applied to consumer products to identify some of the ions present. After you carry out the tests for cations and anions, you may prepare a solution of a consumer product, and carry out the same tests.

Lab Information

Time: $2^1/_2$ hr

Comments: Use several small beakers to hold the reagents. Be sure to label each.
              HCl and HNO₃ are strong acids, and NaOH is a strong base. Handle with care!
              If they are spilled on the skin, rinse thoroughly with water for 10 minutes.
              Dispose of test results properly.
              Tear out the report sheets and place them beside the matching procedures.

Related Topics: Ions, chemical change, solubility rules

Experimental Procedures

WEAR YOUR GOGGLES!

A. Tests for Positive Ions (Cations)

Materials: Spot plate, Bunsen burner, test tubes and test tube rack, flame-test wire, 4 small beakers, 3 M HCl, 6 M HNO₃, 6 M NaOH, dropper bottles of 0.1 M NaCl, 0.1 M KCl, 0.1 M CaCl₂, 0.1 M (NH₄)₂C₂O₄ (ammonium oxalate), 0.1 M NH₄Cl, 0.1 M FeCl₃, 0.1 M KSCN (potassium thiocyanate), red litmus paper, warm water bath, stirring rod

In many parts of this experiment, you will be using 2 mL of different solutions. Place 2 mL of water in the same size test tube that you will be using. As you obtain solutions for the experiment, take a volume that matches the height of the 2 mL of water. Be sure to label each test tube. Many test tubes have a frosted section to write on. If not, use a marking pencil or a label. Before you begin this group of experiments, place about 15 mL of each of the following reagents in small beakers and label them: 3 M HCl, 6 M HNO₃, and 6 M NaOH. Another beaker of distilled water is convenient for rinsing out the droppers.

Preparation of an unknown

Take a small beaker to your instructor for a sample of the unknown salt solution assigned to you. Record the sample number. If the unknown is a solid, dissolve 1 g of the salt in 50 mL of distilled water. Use small portions of this *unknown* solution in each of the tests. You will need to identify the presence of a cation and an anion in the unknown by comparing the test results of the unknown with the test results given by each of the known solutions.

A.1 Flame tests for Na^+, K^+, and Ca^{2+}

Obtain a spot plate and place 5–8 drops of 0.1 M solutions of NaCl, KCl, $CaCl_2$, and your unknown solution into separate wells. Dip the test wire in 3 M HCl and heat the wire until the flame is light blue. Place the wire loop in the NaCl solution and then into the flame. Record the color produced by the Na^+ ion. Clean the wire, and repeat the test with the KCl solution. The color (pink-lavender) of K^+ does not last long, so look for it immediately. Record the color for K^+. Clean the wire again, and repeat the flame test with Ca^{2+}. Record the color of the Ca^{2+} flame.

Testing the unknown Clean the flame-test wire and dip it in the unknown solution. Record the results when the wire is placed in a flame. If there is a color that matches the color of an ion you tested in the flame tests (A.1), you can conclude that you have one of the ions Na^+, K^+, or Ca^{2+} in your unknown. Record. If you think Ca^{2+} is present, you may wish to confirm it with test A.2. If the flame test does not produce any color, then Na^+, K^+, and Ca^{2+} are not present in your unknown.

A.2 Test for calcium ion, Ca^{2+}

Place 2 mL of 0.1 M $CaCl_2$ in a test tube and 2 mL of your unknown solution in another test tube. Add 15 drops of ammonium oxalate solution, 0.1 M $(NH_4)_2C_2O_4$, to each. Look for a cloudy, white solid (precipitate). If the solution remains clear, place the test tube in a warm water bath for 5 minutes, then look for a precipitate. The net equation for the reaction is

$$Ca^{2+} + C_2O_4{}^{2-} \longrightarrow CaC_2O_4(s)$$

A white precipitate indicates the presence of Ca^{2+}.

A.3 Test for ammonium ion, $NH_4{}^+$

Place 2 mL of 0.1 M NH_4Cl in a test tube and 2 mL of your unknown in another test tube. Add 15 drops of 6 M NaOH to each. *Carefully* fan the vapors from the test tube toward you. You may notice the odor of ammonia. Place a strip of moistened red litmus paper across the top of the test tube and set the test tube in a warm water bath. The $NH_3(g)$ given off will turn the red litmus paper blue.

$$NH_4{}^+ + OH^- \longrightarrow NH_3(g) + H_2O$$

Ammonia

Repeat the test with your unknown. Record results.

A.4 Test for ferric ion, Fe^{3+}

Place 2 mL of 0.1 M $FeCl_3$ in a test tube and 2 mL of your unknown in another test tube. Add 5 drops of 6 M HNO_3 and 2–3 drops of potassium thiocyanate, 0.1 M KSCN. A deep red color indicates that Fe^{3+} is present. A faint pink color is *not* a positive test for iron. Repeat the test with your unknown. Record results.

$$Fe^{3+} + 3SCN^- \longrightarrow Fe(SCN)_3$$

Deep red color

B. Tests for Negative Ions (Anions)

Materials: Test tubes, test tube rack, 0.1 M NaCl, 0.1 M AgNO$_3$ (dropper bottle), 3 M HCl, 6 M HNO$_3$, stirring rod, 0.1 M Na$_2$SO$_4$, 0.1 M BaCl$_2$, 0.1 M Na$_3$PO$_4$, (NH$_4$)$_2$MoO$_4$ (ammonium molybdate reagent), 0.1 M Na$_2$CO$_3$, hot water bath

B.1 **Test for chloride ion, Cl$^-$** Place 2 mL of 0.1 M NaCl solution in a test tube and 2 mL of your unknown in another test tube. To each sample, add 5–10 drops of 0.1 M AgNO$_3$ and 10 drops of 6 M HNO$_3$. Stir with a glass stirring rod. *Caution: AgNO$_3$ stains the skin.* Any white solid that remains is AgCl(s). Any white solids that dissolve with HNO$_3$ do not contain Cl$^-$. Record the results of your known and unknown.

$$Ag^+ \ + \ Cl^- \ \longrightarrow \ AgCl(s)$$
White precipitate remains after HNO$_3$ is added.

B.2 **Test for sulfate ion, SO$_4^{2-}$** Place 2 mL of 0.1 M Na$_2$SO$_4$ solution in a test tube and 2 mL of your unknown in another test tube. Add 1 mL (20 drops) of BaCl$_2$ and 5–6 drops of 6 M HNO$_3$ to each test tube. BaSO$_4$, a white precipitate, does not dissolve in HNO$_3$. Other anions, CO$_3^{2-}$ and PO$_4^{3-}$, will also form barium compounds, Ba$_3$(PO$_4$)$_2$ and BaCO$_3$, but they will *dissolve* in HNO$_3$. Record your test results for the known and unknown.

B.3 **Test for phosphate ion, PO$_4^{3-}$** Place 2 mL of 0.1 M Na$_3$PO$_4$ solution in a test tube and 2 mL of your unknown in another test tube. Add 10 drops of 6 M HNO$_3$ to each. After the test tubes are warmed in a hot water bath (60°C), add 15 drops of ammonium molybdate solution, (NH$_4$)$_2$MoO$_4$. The formation of a yellow precipitate indicates the presence of PO$_4^{3-}$. Record the test results of the known and the unknown.

B.4 **Test for carbonate ion, CO$_3^{2-}$** Place 2 mL of 0.1 M Na$_2$CO$_3$ solution in a test tube and 2 mL of your unknown in another test tube. *While carefully observing the solution*, add 10 drops of 3 M HCl to each sample. Watch for a strong evolution of bubbles of CO$_2$ gas as you add the HCl. The gas bubbles are formed quickly, and may be overlooked. If gas bubbles were not observed, add another 15–20 drops of HCl *as you watch the solution*. Record your results for the known and the unknown.

$$Na_2CO_3(aq) \ + \ 2HCl(aq) \ \longrightarrow \ CO_2(g) \ + \ H_2O \ + \ 2NaCl(aq)$$
Gas bubbles

C. Writing the Formula of Your Unknown Salt

Your unknown solution was made from a salt composed of a cation and an anion. From your test results, you can identify one of the cations (Na$^+$, K$^+$, Ca^{2+}, NH$_4^+$, or Fe^{3+}) and one of the anions (Cl$^-$, SO$_4^{2-}$, PO$_4^{3-}$, or CO$_3^{2-}$). For example, if you found that in the cation tests you got the same test result as for Ca^{2+} and in the anion tests you got the same result as for Cl$^-$, then the ions in your unknown salt would be Ca^{2+} and Cl$^-$. The formula CaCl$_2$ is written using charge balance.

C.1 Write the symbols and names of the cation and anion that were present in your unknown.

C.2 Use the ionic charges of the cation and anion to write the formula and name of the salt that was your unknown.

D. Testing Consumer Products for Some Cations and Anions

The tests in this experiment may be used to identify ions in samples of the following consumer products. Perhaps you have other ideas for products to test. Ask your instructor. In many of the products, there will be several cations and anions that give positive tests. Describe your results on the lab report.

Product	Procedure
Juices	Obtain 25-30 mL of a light-color fruit juice. If it contains pulp or fiber, filter first. Use 2-3 mL of the final solution for each of the cation and anion tests.
Sodas	Obtain 25-30 mL of a soft drink, or mineral water. For colas, root beers, or others with deep colors, mix the soft drink with a small amount of charcoal in a small beaker. Charcoal will absorb the dyes. Filter and use 2-3 mL of the filtrate for each cation or anion test.
Milk	Obtain 30 mL of nonfat milk. Add 10 mL of 0.1 M acetic acid ($HC_2H_3O_2$). Small particles of protein(curds) will form. Filter. Gently boil the filtrate to reduce the volume to 15-20 mL. Use 2-3 mL of the filtrate for each cation or anion test
Bone meal or plant food granules	In a beaker, mix a scoop of bone meal or plant food with 15 mL distilled water water and 15 mL of 6M HNO_3. Heat gently (DO NOT BOIL) until most of the material dissolves. Cool and filter. Use 2-3 mL of the filtrate for each cation or anion test
Window cleaner	Obtain 20-25 mL of a window cleaner. Use 2-3 mL of the filtrate for each cation or anion test

Report Sheet

Date _____   Name _____

Section _____   Team _____

Instructor _____

Pre-Lab Study Questions

1. How can the presence of an ion in a solution be detected?

2. If a reaction produces an insoluble salt, what will you notice happening in the test tube?

A. Tests for Positive Ions (Cations)

Unknown number _____

Procedure	Cation Tested	Observations	Observations for Unknown
A.1 **Flame tests**	Na^+		
	K^+		
	Ca^{2+}		
A.2 **Oxalate test**	Ca^{2+}		
A.3 **Ammonium test**	NH_4^+		
A.4 **Iron test**	Fe^{3+}		

Identification of the positive ion in the unknown solution
From your test results, what positive ion (cation) is present in your unknown? _____
Explain your choice.

109

Report Sheet

B. Tests for Negative Ions (Anions)

Procedure	Anion Tested	Observations	Observations for Unknown
B.1 Chloride test	Cl^-		
B.2 Sulfate test	SO_4^{2-}		
B.3 Phosphate test	PO_4^{3-}		
B.4 Carbonate test	CO_3^{2-}		

Identification of the negative ion in the unknown solution
From your test results, what negative ion (anion) is present in your unknown? _____
Explain your choice.

C. Writing the Formula of Your Unknown Salt

Unknown sample number _____

C.1 Cation _____   Name _____

Anion _____   Name _____

C.2 Formula of the unknown salt   _____

Name of the unknown salt   _____

Report Sheet

D. Testing Consumer Products for Some Cations and Anions

Product tested _____

Cation tests	Results	Ion present
Flame tests (Na^+, K^+, Ca^{2+})		
Ca^{2+}		
NH_4^+		
Fe^{3+}		
Anion tests		
Cl^-		
SO_4^{2-}		
PO_4^{3-}		
CO_3^{2-}		

Report Sheet

Questions and Problems

Q.1 How do the tests on known solutions containing cations and anions make it possible for you to identify the cations or anions in an unknown substance?

Q.2 You have a solution that is composed of either NaCl or $CaCl_2$. What tests would you run to identify the compound?

Q.3 If tap water turns a deep red color with a few drops of KSCN, what cation is present?

Q.4 A plant food contains $(NH_4)_3PO_4$. What tests would you run to verify the presence of the NH_4^+ ion and the PO_4^{3-} ion?

Q.5 Write the symbol of the cation or anion that give(s) the following reaction:

_____ a. Forms a precipitate with $AgNO_3$ that does not dissolve in HNO_3

_____ b. Forms a gas with HCl

_____ c. Gives a bright, yellow-orange flame test

_____ d. Forms a precipitate with $BaCl_2$ that does not dissolve in HNO_3

Solutions, Colloids, and Suspensions

Goals

- Perform chemical tests for chloride, glucose, and starch.
- Use dialysis to distinguish between solutions and colloids.
- Separate colloids from suspensions.
- Discuss the effects of hypotonic and hypertonic solutions on red blood cells.

Discussion

A. Identification Tests

A chemical test helps us identify the presence or absence of a substance in a solution. In a *positive test,* the chemical change indicates the substance is present. In a *negative test,* there is no chemical reaction and the substance is absent.

B. Osmosis and Dialysis

Osmosis occurs when water moves through the walls of red blood cells, which are semipermeable membranes. The osmotic pressure of an *isotonic* solution is the same as that of red blood cells. Both 0.9% NaCl (saline) and 5% glucose solutions are considered isotonic to the cells of the body. In isotonic solution, the flow of water into and out of the red blood cells is equal. A *hypotonic* solution has a lower osmotic pressure than an isotonic solution; the osmotic pressure of a *hypertonic* solution is greater. In either case, the flow of water in and out of the cell is no longer equal, and the cell volume is altered.

When red blood cells are placed in a strong salt solution, they form small clumps. This process, called *crenation,* occurs because water diffuses out of the cells into the more concentrated salt solution. If red blood cells are placed in water, they expand and may rupture. This process, called *hemolysis,* occurs because water diffuses into the cells where there is a higher solute concentration. In both cases, osmosis has occurred as water passed through a semipermeable membrane into the more concentrated solution.

In *dialysis,* small particles and water, but not colloids, move across a semipermeable membrane from their high concentrations to low. Many of the membranes in the body are dialyzing membranes. For example, the intestinal tract consists of a semipermeable membrane that allows the solution particles from digestion to pass into the blood and lymph. Larger, incompletely digested food particles that are colloidal size or larger remain within the intestinal wall. Dialyzing membranes are also used in hemodialysis to separate waste particles, particularly urea, out of the blood.

C. Filtration

In the process of *filtration,* gravity separates suspension particles from the solvent. The pores in the filter paper are smaller than the size of the suspension particles, causing the suspension particles to be trapped in the filter paper. The colloidal particles and the solution particles are smaller and can pass through the pores in the filter paper.

In this experiment, a mixture of starch, NaCl, glucose, and charcoal is poured into filter paper. Using identification tests, the substances that remain in the filter paper and the substances that pass through the filter paper can be determined.

From *Laboratory Manual for General, Organic, & Biological Chemistry,* Karen C. Timberlake. Copyright © 2002 Pearson Education, Inc., publishing as Benjamin Cummings. All rights reserved.

Lab Information

Time: $2^1/_2$ hr
Comments: Label the containers to keep track of different solutions.
              Tear out the report sheets and place them beside the matching procedures.
Related Topics: Solutions, colloids, suspensions, osmosis, hypertonic solutions, isotonic solutions,
              hypotonic solutions, dialysis

Experimental Procedures

WEAR YOUR SAFETY GOGGLES!

A.   Identification Tests

Materials: Three small beakers (100–150 mL), test tubes (6), test tube rack, stirring rod,
          50-mL graduated cylinder, test tube holder, droppers, boiling water bath, 1% starch,
          10% NaCl, 0.1 M $AgNO_3$, 10% glucose, Benedict's reagent, iodine reagent. *Dropper
          bottles with these reagents may be available in the laboratory.*

In this experiment, you will perform the identification tests for Cl^-, glucose, and starch. To determine the
presence or absence of Cl^-, glucose, or starch in later experiments, refer to the results of the tests. For
each test, observe and record the initial properties of the reagent and the final appearance of the solution
after the reagent is added. In a positive test, there will be a change in the original properties of the
reagent, such as a color change and/or the formation of a precipitate (opaque solid). If there is no change
in the appearance of the reagent, the test is *negative.*

Place small amounts of the reagents for these identification tests in small beakers or vials for use
throughout this experiment. Place 3 mL of water in a test tube for volume comparison. Obtain 3–4 mL of
0.1 M $AgNO_3$, 20–25 mL of Benedict's reagent, 4–5 mL of iodine reagent, and 10 mL of distilled water.
Label each container. Keep these reagent containers at your desk for the duration of the experiment.

Caution: $AgNO_3$ and iodine reagent stain!

A.1 **Chloride (Cl^-) test** Place 3 mL of 10% NaCl in a test tube. Place 3 mL of distilled water in anoth-
     er test tube. The test tube with the water will be the control or comparison sample. Test for Cl^- by
     adding 2 drops of 0.1 M $AgNO_3$ to each. Record your observations. Compare the results for the
     NaCl solution with the results for the water sample.

A.2 **Starch test** Place 3 mL of 1% starch solution in a test tube. Place 3 mL of distilled water in
     another test tube. Add 2–3 drops of iodine reagent to each. Record your observations. Compare the
     results for the starch sample with the results for the water sample.

A.3 **Glucose test** Place 3 mL of 10% glucose solution in a test tube. Place 3 mL of distilled water in
     another test tube. Add 3 mL of Benedict's reagent to the glucose and to the distilled water. Heat
     both test tubes in a boiling water bath for 5 minutes. Record your observations. Compare the results
     for the glucose with the results for the water sample. *Note: Each time you carry out the glucose
     test, the test tubes containing Benedict's reagent must be heated in a boiling water bath.*

B. Osmosis and Dialysis

Materials: Cellophane tube (15–20 cm), test tubes (3), test tube rack, test tube holder, stirring rod, droppers, 50-mL graduated cylinder, funnel, 100-mL beaker, 250-mL beaker, boiling water bath, 10% NaCl, 10% glucose, 1% starch, 0.1 M $AgNO_3$, Benedict's solution, iodine reagent

In a small beaker, combine 10 mL of 10% NaCl, 10 mL of 10% glucose, and 10 mL of 1% starch solution. Tie a knot in one end of a piece of cellophane tubing (dialysis bag). Place a funnel in the open end and pour in about 20 mL of the mixture. Save the rest of the mixture for part C. Tie a firm knot in the open end to close the dialysis bag. Rinse the dialysis bag with distilled water. Place the dialysis bag in a 250-mL beaker and cover with distilled water. See Figure 1.

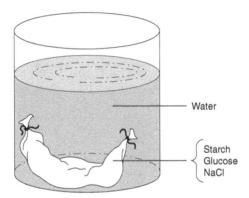

Figure 1   Dialysis bag placed in distilled water

Pour off 15 mL of the distilled water surrounding the bag for the first group of tests. Divide the 15 mL into three test tubes (5 mL each). Repeat the tests from part A. A substance is present in the water outside the dialysis bag if a test for that substance gives the same results as in the identification tests in part A. Record the result as positive (+). If the substance is absent (there is no chemical reaction), record that test as negative (−).

Identification Tests:

Test for Cl⁻	Add $AgNO_3$ to the dialysis water in the first test tube.
Test for starch	Add iodine reagent to the dialysis water in the second test tube.
Test for glucose	Add Benedict's solution to the dialysis water in the third test tube. Heat.

After 20 minutes and 40 minutes, pour off another 15 mL of water from *outside* the dialysis bag. Separate the water sample into three test tubes and test again for Cl⁻, starch, and glucose. Record your test results each time.

After the 40-minute test, break the bag open, and test 15 mL of its contents. From your results, determine which substance(s) dialyzed through the membrane, and which substance(s) did not. *Save the remainder of the bag's contents for use in part C.*

C. Filtration

Materials: Funnel, filter paper, 50-mL graduated cylinder, test tubes (3), test tube rack, test tube holder, stirring rod, droppers, two 150-mL beakers, boiling water bath, powdered charcoal, iodine reagent, 0.1 M $AgNO_3$, Benedict's solution

To the mixture of glucose, NaCl, and starch from part B, add a small amount of powdered charcoal. Fold a piece of filter paper in half and in half again. Open the fold to give a cone-like shape and place the filter paper cone in a funnel. Push it gently against the sides and moisten with water. Place a small beaker under the funnel. Pour the mixture into the filter paper. Collect the liquid (filtrate) that passes through the filter. See Figure 2.

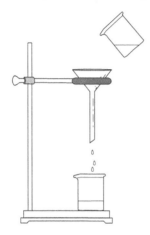

Figure 2 Filtering a mixture

C.1 Describe what you see in the filter paper.

C.2 Test the liquid in the beaker (filtrate) for chloride, starch, and glucose using the identification tests from part A. Compare the results of each test to part A. Use the test results to identify the substances that passed through the filter paper.

C.3 From the test results, determine what was trapped in the filter and what passed through. Identify the substance that is a suspension.

Report Sheet

Date _____   Name _____

Section _____   Team _____

Instructor _____

Pre-Lab Study Questions

1. In making pickles, a cucumber is placed in a strong salt solution. Explain what happens.

2. Why is it important that cell membranes are semipermeable membranes?

3. What is the difference between osmosis and dialysis?

4. How does an artificial kidney separate waste products from the blood?

A. Identification Tests

Test	Reagent Added	Results of Positive Test	Results with Water Control
A.1 Cl⁻	$AgNO_3$		
A.2 **Starch**	Iodine		
A.3 **Glucose**	Benedict's; heat		

Report Sheet

B. Osmosis and Dialysis

Test Results of Water Outside Dialysis Bag

Time	Cl⁻ Present?	Starch Present?	Glucose Present?
0 minutes			
20 minutes			
40 minutes			
Contents of dialysis bag			

Questions and Problems

Q.1 Which substance(s) were found in the water *outside* the dialysis bag?

Q.2 How did those substance(s) go into the water outside the dialysis bag?

Q.3 What substance(s) were retained inside the dialysis bag? Why were they retained?

C. Filtration

C.1 Appearance of filter paper _____

Substance present   _____

C.2 Test for	Results of Test	Substance Present in Filtrate?
Cl⁻		
Starch		
Glucose		

C.3 Which substance is a suspension?   _____

Which substances are solutions or colloids?   _____

Report Sheet

Questions and Problems

Q.4 What is an isotonic solution?

What is a hypotonic solution?

What is a hypertonic solution?

Q.5 State whether each of the following are isotonic, hypotonic, or hypertonic:

a. H_2O _____

b. 0.9% NaCl   _____

c. 10% glucose   _____

d. 3% NaCl   _____

e. 0.2% NaCl   _____

Q.6 A red blood cell in a hypertonic solution will shrink in volume as it undergoes *crenation*. In a hypotonic solution, a red blood cell will swell and possibly burst as it undergoes *hemolysis*. Predict the effect on a red blood cell (crenation, hemolysis, or none) that the following solutions would have:

a. 2% NaCl   _____

b. H_2O _____

c. 5% glucose   _____

d. 1% glucose   _____

e. 10% glucose   _____

Q.7 A parenteral solution is a solution that is injected into the tissues or bloodstream, but not given orally. Why are isotonic solutions used as parenteral solutions?

Acids, Bases, pH, and Buffers

Goals

- Prepare a naturally occurring dye to use as a pH indicator.
- Measure the pH of several substances using cabbage indicator and a pH meter.
- Calculate pH from the $[H^+]$ or the $[OH^-]$ of a solution.
- Calculate the molar concentration and percentage of acetic acid in vinegar.
- Observe the changes in pH as acid or base is added to buffered and unbuffered solutions.
- Calculate pH from the $[H^+]$ or the $[OH^-]$ of a solution.

Discussion

An *acid* is a substance that dissolves in water and donates a hydrogen ion, or proton (H^+), to water. In the laboratory we have been using acids such as hydrochloric acid (HCl) and nitric acid (HNO_3).

$$HCl \ + \ H_2O \ \longrightarrow \ H_3O^+ + Cl^-$$
$$\textit{hydronium ion}$$

You use acids and bases every day. There are acids in oranges, lemons, vinegar, and bleach. In this experiment we will use acetic acid ($HC_2H_3O_2$). Acetic acid is the acid in vinegar that gives it a sour taste.

A *base* is a substance that accepts a proton. Some household bases include ammonia, detergents, and oven-cleaning products. Some typical bases used in the laboratory are sodium hydroxide (NaOH) and potassium hydroxide (KOH). Most of the common bases dissolve in water and produce hydroxide ions, OH^-.

$$NaOH \ \longrightarrow \ Na^+ \ + \ OH^-$$

An important weak base found in the laboratory and in some household cleaners is ammonia. In water, it reacts to form ammonium and hydroxide ions:

$$NH_3 \ + \ H_2O \ \longrightarrow \ NH_4^+ \ + \ OH^-$$

In a *neutralization* reaction, the protons (H^+) from the acid combine with hydroxide ions (OH^-) from the base to produce water (H_2O). The remaining substance is a salt, which is composed of ions from the acid and base. For example, the neutralization of HCl by NaOH is written as

$$HCl \ + \ NaOH \ \longrightarrow \ NaCl \ + \ H_2O$$

If we write the ionic substances in the equation as ions, we see that the H^+ and the OH^- form water.

$$H^+ \ + \ Cl^- \ + \ Na^+ \ + \ OH^- \ \longrightarrow \ Na^+ \ + \ Cl^- \ + \ H_2O$$

$$H^+ \qquad\qquad + \ OH^- \ \longrightarrow \ H_2O$$

In a complete neutralization, the amount of H^+ will be equal to the amount of OH^-.

From *Laboratory Manual for General, Organic, & Biological Chemistry,* Karen C. Timberlake. Copyright © 2002 Pearson Education, Inc., publishing as Benjamin Cummings. All rights reserved.

A. pH Color Using Red Cabbage Indicator

The pH of a solution tells us whether a solution is acidic, basic, or neutral. On the pH scale, pH values below 7 are acidic, equal to 7 is neutral, and values above 7 are basic. Typically, the pH scale has values between 0 and 14.

pH scale

0   1   2   3   4   5   6   7   8   9   10   11   12   13   14

← —————— *acidic* ————→ *neutral* ← —————— *basic* ————→

Many natural substances contain dyes that produce distinctive colors at different pH values. By extracting (removing) the dye from red cabbage leaves, a natural indicator can be prepared. Adding the red cabbage solution to solutions of a variety of acids and bases will produce a series of distinctive colors. When the red cabbage solution is added to a test sample, the color produced can be matched to the colors of the pH reference set to determine the pH of the sample. A pH meter can also be used to measure pH.

B. Measuring pH

The concentration (moles/liter, indicated by brackets [ ]) of H_3O^+ or OH^- can be determined from the ionization constant for water (K_w). In pure water, $[H_3O^+] = [OH^-] = 1 \times 10^{-7}$ M.

$$K_w = [H_3O^+][OH^-] = [1 \times 10^{-7}][1 \times 10^{-7}] = 1 \times 10^{-14}$$

If the $[H_3O^+]$ or $[OH^-]$ for an acid or a base is known, the other can be calculated. For example, an acid has a $[H^+] = 1 \times 10^{-4}$ M. We can find the $[OH^-]$ of the solution by solving the K_w expression for $[OH^-]$:

$$[OH^{\pm}] = \frac{1 \times 10^{\pm 14}}{[H_3O^+]} = \frac{1 \times 10^{\pm 14}}{1 \times 10^{\pm 4}} = 1 \times 10^{\pm 10} \text{ M}$$

The pH of a solution is a measure of its $[H_3O^+]$. It is defined as the negative log of the hydrogen ion concentration.

$$pH = -\log [H_3O^+]$$

Therefore, a solution with a $[H_3O^+] = 1 \times 10^{-4}$ M has a pH of 4.0, and is acidic. A solution with a $[H_3O^+] = 1 \times 10^{-11}$ M has a pH of 11.0, and is basic.

C. Effect of Buffers on pH

The pH of the blood is maintained between 7.35 and 7.45 by buffers in the body. If blood pH goes above or below that range, it can destroy the cells in the blood. *Buffers* maintain the pH of a solution by reacting with small amounts of acids or bases. Many buffers contain a weak acid and its salt. The weak acid reacts with excess base, and the anion of the salt picks up excess H^+. It is the ability of a buffer to react with added acid or base that maintains the pH of a solution. The pH of the blood is kept constant by the bicarbonate buffer, which is carbonic acid, H_2CO_3 (weak acid), and bicarbonate anion, HCO_3^- (salt). When base (OH^-) is added, it reacts with the weak acid in the buffer and produces bicarbonate ion and water:

$$H_2CO_3 + OH^- \longrightarrow HCO_3^- + H_2O$$

When acid (H^+) enters the blood, it reacts with the HCO_3^- anion and re-forms carbonic acid:

$$HCO_3^- + H^+ \longrightarrow H_2CO_3$$

In this experiment, the effect of an acid and a base on the pH of a buffer and a nonbuffer will be determined.

Lab Information

Time: 2¹/₂ hr
Comments: Students may be asked to bring a red cabbage to class.
                    Share test tubes with your lab neighbors to prepare the pH reference solutions.
                    Tear out the report sheets and place them beside the matching procedures.
Related Topics: Acids, bases, pH, buffers

Experimental Procedures

A. pH Color Using Red Cabbage Indicator

Materials: Red cabbage leaves, 400-mL beaker, distilled water, Bunsen burner or hot plate, 150-mL beaker, test tubes, two test tube racks, set of buffers with pH ranging from 1 to 13

Using a 150-mL beaker, obtain 50 mL of cabbage dye indicator. The indicator can be prepared by placing 5 or 6 torn leaves from red cabbage in a 400-mL beaker. Add about 150–200 mL of distilled water to cover the leaves. Heat on a hot plate or using a Bunsen burner, but do not boil. When the solution has attained a dark purple color, turn off the burner and cool.

Preparation of a pH reference set Arrange 13 test tubes in two test tube racks. You may need to combine your test tube set with your neighbor's set. (Your instructor may prepare a pH reference set for the entire class.) Pour 3–4 mL of each buffer in a separate test tube to create a set with pH values of 1–13. **Caution: Low pH values are strongly acidic; high pH values are strongly basic. Work with care.** To each test tube, add 2–3 mL of the *cooled* red cabbage solution. If you wish a deeper color, add more cabbage solution. Describe the colors of the pH solutions. ***Keep this reference set for the next part of the experiment.***

B. Measuring pH

Materials: Shell vials or test tubes, samples to test for pH (shampoo, conditioner, mouthwash, antacids, detergents, fruit juice, vinegar, cleaners, aspirin, etc.), cabbage juice indicator from part A, pH meter, calibration buffers, wash bottle, Kimwipes™

Place 3–4 mL of a sample in a shell vial (or a test tube). Add 2–3 mL of red cabbage solution. Describe the color and compare to the colors of the pH reference set. The pH of the buffer in the reference set that gives the best color match is the pH of the sample. Record. Test several samples.

pH Meter Your instructor will demonstrate the use of the pH meter and calibrate it with a known pH buffer. After you determine the pH of a sample using the red cabbage solution, take the sample to a pH meter, and record the pH. Rinse off the electrode with distilled water.

C. Effect of Buffers on pH

Materials: Buffer with a high pH (9–11), buffer with a low pH (3–4), droppers, shell vials or test tubes, 0.1 M NaCl, 0.1 M HCl, 0.1 M NaOH, pH meter, cabbage juice indicator from part A

Effect of Adding Acid

C.1 Place 10.0 mL of one of the following solutions into a shell vial (or test tube):
a. H_2O
b. 0.1 M NaCl
c. A buffer with a high pH
d. A buffer with a low pH

Add 2–3 mL of cabbage indicator. Describe the color. Determine the pH of each sample using the pH reference set or pH meter, or both. Record.

C.2 Add 5 drops of 0.1 M HCl (acid). Stir and determine the pH. Record. Add 5 more drops of 0.1 M HCl. Record any color change in the indicator. Determine the pH. Repeat this procedure with each of the other solutions.

C.3 Determine the change in pH, if any. Identify the solutions that are buffers.

Effect of Adding Base

C.4 Place 10.0 mL of one of the following solutions into a shell vial (or test tube):
a. H_2O
b. 0.1 M NaCl
c. A buffer with a high pH
d. A buffer with a low pH

Add 2–3 mL of cabbage indicator. Describe the color. Determine the pH of each sample using the pH reference set or pH meter, or both. Record.

C.5 Add 5 drops of 0.1 M NaOH (base). Stir and determine the pH. Record. Add 5 more drops of 0.1 M NaOH. Record any color change in the indicator. Determine the pH. Repeat this procedure with the other samples listed in C.4.

C.6 Determine the change in pH, if any. Identify the solutions that are buffers.

Report Sheet

Date _____   Name _____

Section _____   Team _____

Instructor _____

Pre-Lab Study Questions

1. What does the pH of a solution tell you?

2. What is neutralization?

3. What is a buffer?

A. pH Colors Using Red Cabbage Indicator

pH	Colors of Acidic Solutions
1	
2	
3	
4	
5	
6	

pH	Colors of Basic Solutions
8	
9	
10	
11	
12	
13	

pH	Color of Neutral Solution
7	

Report Sheet

B. Measuring pH

Substance	Color with Indicator	pH Using Indicator	pH Using pH Meter	Acidic, Basic, or Neutral?
Household cleaners				
vinegar				
ammonia				
Drinks, juices				
lemon juice				
apple juice				
Detergents, shampoos				
shampoo				
detergent				
hair conditioner				
Health aids				
mouthwash				
antacid				
aspirin				
Other items				

Report Sheet

Questions and Problems

Q.1 Complete the following table:

$[H_3O^+]$	$[OH^-]$	pH	Acidic, Basic, or Neutral?
1×10^{-6}			
		10.0	
	1×10^{-3}		
			Neutral

Q.2 The label on the shampoo claims that it is pH balanced. What do you think "pH balanced" means?

Q.3 A solution has a $[OH^-] = 1 \times 10^{-5}$ M. What are the $[H_3O^+]$ and the pH of the solution?

Q.4 A sample of 0.0020 mole of HCl is dissolved in water to make a 2000-mL solution. Calculate the molarity of the HCl solution, the $[H_3O^+]$, and the pH. For a strong acid such as HCl, the $[H_3O^+]$ is the same as the molarity of the HCl solution.

$$HCl + H_2O \longrightarrow H_3O^+ + Cl^-$$

Report Sheet

C. Effect of Buffers on pH

Effect of adding 0.1 M HCl

C.1 Solution	C.2 pH after Initial pH	pH after 10 5 drops HCl	C.3 drops HCl	pH change	Buffer?
H_2O					
0.1 M NaCl					
High pH buffer					
Low pH buffer					

Effect of adding 0.1 M NaOH

Solution	C.4 Initial pH	C.5 pH after 5 drops NaOH	pH after 10 drops NaOH	C.6 pH change	Buffer?
H_2O					
0.1 M NaCl					
High pH buffer					
Low pH buffer					

Questions and Problems

Q.5 Which solution(s) showed the greatest change in pH? Why?

Q.6 Which solutions(s) showed little or no change in pH? Why?

Q.7 Is a buffer supposed to keep the pH of a solution at 7 (neutral)?

Q.8 Normally, the pH of the human body is fixed in a very narrow range between 7.35 and 7.45. A patient with an acidotic blood pH of 7.3 may be treated with an alkali such as sodium bicarbonate. Why would this treatment raise the pH of the blood?

Properties of Organic Compounds

Goals

- Observe chemical and physical properties of organic and inorganic compounds.
- Identity functional groups in three-dimensional models.

Discussion

A. Color, Odor, and Physical State

Organic compounds are made of carbon and hydrogen, and sometimes oxygen and nitrogen. Of all the elements, only carbon atoms bond to many more carbon atoms, a unique ability that gives rise to many more organic compounds than all the inorganic compounds known today. The covalent bonds in organic compounds and the ionic bonds in inorganic compounds account for several of the differences we will observe in their physical and chemical properties. See Table 1.

Table 1 *Comparing Some Properties of Organic and Inorganic Compounds*

Organic Compounds	Inorganic Compounds
Covalent bonds	Ionic or polar bonds
Soluble in nonpolar solvents, not water	Soluble in water
Low melting and boiling points	High melting and boiling points
Strong, distinct odors	Usually no odor
Poor or nonconductors of electricity	Good conductors of electricity
Flammable	Not flammable

B. Solubility

Typically, inorganic compounds that are ionic are soluble in water, a polar compound, but organic compounds are nonpolar and thus are not soluble in water. However, organic compounds are soluble in organic solvents because they are both nonpolar. A general rule for solubility is that "like dissolves like."

C. Combustion

Many organic compounds react with oxygen, a reaction called *combustion,* to form carbon dioxide and water. Combustion is the reaction that occurs when gasoline burns with oxygen in the engine of a car or when natural gas, methane, burns in a heater or stove. In a combustion reaction, heat is given off; the reaction is exothermic. Equations for the combustion of methane and propane are written as follows:

$$CH_4(g) \; + \; 2O_2(g) \longrightarrow \; CO_2(g) \; + \; 2H_2O(g) \; + \; heat$$
methane

$$C_3H_8(g) \; + \; 5O_2(g) \longrightarrow \; 3CO_2(g) \; + \; 4H_2O(g) \; + \; heat$$
propane

D. Functional Groups

Although there are millions of organic compounds, they can be classified according to organic families. Each family contains a characteristic structural feature called a functional group, which is a certain atom or group of atoms that give similar physical and chemical properties to that family. Because the organic compounds in a family contain the same functional group, they undergo the same types of chemical reactions. In this lab, we will take a look at some of the common functional groups that allow us to classify organic compounds according to the structure,

Alkanes, alkenes, and alkynes are hydrocarbons that consist of only carbon and hydrogen atoms. Alkanes contain carbon-carbon single bonds, whereas alkenes contain one or more carbon-carbon double bonds, and alkynes contain a carbon-carbon triple bond. To write a condensed structural formula, the hydrogen atoms attached to each carbon are written adjacent to the symbol C for carbon. Thus, a CH_3- is the abbreviation for a carbon attached to three hydrogen atoms, whereas $-CH_2-$ shows a carbon attached to two hydrogen atoms.

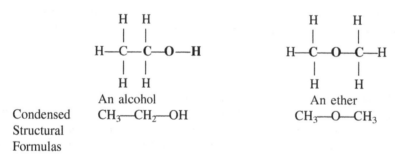

	An alkane	An alkene	An alkyne
Condensed Structural Formulas	$CH_3{-}CH_3$	$CH_2{=}CH_2$	$HC{\equiv}CH$

Alcohols and ethers contain an oxygen atom. Alcohols have a *hydroxyl group*, which is an $-OH$ group, bonded to a carbon atom. In an ether, the oxygen atom is bonded to two carbon atoms.

	An alcohol	An ether
Condensed Structural Formulas	$CH_3{-}CH_2{-}OH$	$CH_3{-}O{-}CH_3$

Aldehydes and ketones, contain a carbonyl group, which is a carbon-oxygen double bond (C=O). In an aldehyde, the carbon bonds to at least one hydrogen atom. In a ketone, the carbon in the carbonyl group bonds to two other carbon atoms.

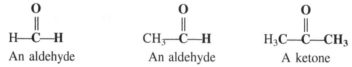

An aldehyde   An aldehyde   A ketone

Carboxylic acids and esters contain the functional group is the carboxyl group, which is a combination of a carbonyl and hydroxyl group. In a carboxylic acid, the oxygen is bonded to a hydrogen atom, whereas in an ester the oxygen is bonded to a carbon and not to hydrogen.

$$\underset{\text{A carboxylic acid}}{CH_3\overset{\overset{\displaystyle O}{\|}}{-}C-O-H} \qquad \text{or} \qquad CH_3COOH \qquad \text{or} \qquad CH_3CO_2H$$

$$\underset{\text{An ester}}{CH_3\overset{\overset{\displaystyle O}{\|}}{-}C-O-CH_3} \qquad \text{or} \qquad CH_3COOCH_3 \qquad \text{or} \qquad CH_3CO_2CH_3$$

Amines contain a nitrogen atom because they are derivatives of ammonia, NH_3. In an amine, one or more carbon groups replace the hydrogen atoms in ammonia. Amines are classified as primary, secondary, or tertiary according to the number of carbon groups bonded to the nitrogen atoms.

NH_3	CH_3-NH_2	CH_3-NH	CH_3-N-CH_3
		$\|$	$\|$
		CH_3	CH_3
Ammonia	A primary amine (1°)	A secondary amine (2°)	A tertiary amine (3°)

Lab Information

Time: 2 hr

Comments: Tear out the report sheets and place them next to the matching procedures. ***Organic compounds are extremely flammable! Use of the Bunsen burner is prohibited.***

Related Topics: Organic compounds, hydrocarbons, solubility, combustion, complete structural formula, functional groups

Experimental Procedures   *Wear your safety goggles!*

A.   Color, Odor, and Physical State *(This may be a lab display.)*

   Materials: Test tubes (6), test tube rack, spatulas, NaCl(*s*), KI(*s*), toluene, benzoic acid, cyclohexane, water, chemistry handbook

   Place each substance into a separate test tube: a few crystals of NaCl, KI, and benzoic acid, and 10 drops each of cyclohexane, toluene, and water. Or if a display is available, observe the samples in a test tube rack in the hood. Record the formula, physical state (solid, liquid, or gas), and odor of each one. To check for odor, first take a breath and hold it while you gently fan the air above the test tube toward you. Look up the melting point of each compound using a chemistry handbook. Record. State the types of bonds in each as ionic or covalent. Identify each as an organic or inorganic compound.

B.   Solubility *(This may be a demonstration or lab display.)*

Materials: Test tubes, spatulas, NaCl(s), toluene, cyclohexane

Work in the hood: Be sure to work with the compounds such as cyclohexane in ventilation hoods, and then dispose of them in the proper waste containers. Place 10 drops of cyclohexane and 10 drops of water in a test tube. Record your observations. Identify the upper layer and the lower layer.

Place a few crystals of NaCl in one test tube and 10 drops of toluene in another test tube. To each sample, add 15 drops of cyclohexane, a nonpolar solvent. Shake gently or tap the bottom of the test tube to mix. Record whether each substance is soluble (S) or insoluble (I) in cyclohexane.

Repeat the experiment with the two substances, but this time add 15 drops of water, a polar solvent. Record whether each substance is soluble (S) or insoluble (I) in water. Identify each substance as an organic or inorganic compound.

Dispose of organic substances in the proper waste container.

C.   Combustion *(This may be a demonstration by your instructor.)*

Materials: 2 evaporating dishes, spatulas, wood splints, NaCl(s), cyclohexane

Work in the hood: Place a small amount (pea-size) of NaCl in an evaporating dish set in an iron ring. Ignite a splint and hold the flame to the NaCl. Record whether the substance burns. Repeat the experiment using 5 drops of cyclohexane instead of NaCl. If the substance burns, note the color of the flame. Identify each as an organic or inorganic compound.

D.   Functional Groups

Materials: An organic model kit or prepared models of organic compounds

D.1   Observe models of organic compounds listed in the table. Or using an organic model kit, construct ball-and-stick models of each of the compounds. Place wooden dowels or springs in all the holes in the carbon atom (black) and attach hydrogen (yellow) atoms, oxygen atoms (red), or nitrogen atoms (blue) as required to complete the functional group for each. Draw a full structural formula showing all the bonds to each carbon atom.

D.2   Circle the functional group in each structure. Classify the organic compound according to the functional group

Report Sheet

Date _____   Name _____

Section _____   Team _____

Instructor _____

Pre-Lab Study Questions

1. Would you expect an organic compound to be soluble in water? Why?

2. Which is more flammable: an organic or inorganic compound?

A. Color, Odor, and Physical State

Name	Formula	Physical State	Odor	Melting Point	Type of Bonds?	Organic or Inorganic?
Sodium chloride						
Cyclohexane	C_6H_{12}					
Potassium iodide						
Benzoic acid	$C_7H_6O_2$					
Toluene	C_7H_8					
Water						

B. Solubility

In the mixture, water is the _____ layer and cyclohexane is the _____ layer.

Solute	Solubility in Cyclohexane	Solubility in Water	Organic or Inorganic?
NaCl			
Toluene			

Report Sheet

C. Combustion

Compound	Flammable (Color of Flame)	Not Flammable	Organic or Inorganic?
NaCl			
Cyclohexane			

From your observations of the chemical and physical properties of alkanes as organic compounds, complete the following table:

Property	Organic Compounds	Inorganic Compounds
Elements		
Bonding		
Melting points		
Strong odors		
Flammability		
Solubility		

Questions and Problems

Q.1 Describe three properties you can use to distinguish between organic and inorganic compounds.

Q.2 A white solid has no odor, is soluble in water, and is not flammable. Would you expect it to be an organic or an inorganic substance? Why?

Q.3 A clear liquid with a gasoline-like odor forms a layer when added to water. Would you expect it to be an organic or an inorganic substance? Why?

Report Sheet

D. Functional Groups

Compound	D.1 **Full Structural Formula**	D.2 **Organic Family**
CH_3—OH		
CH_3—CH_2—CH_3		
CH_2=CH_2		
CH_3—O—CH_3		
CH_3—NH_2		
$\begin{matrix} O \\ \parallel \\ CH_3\text{—C—OH} \end{matrix}$		
$\begin{matrix} O \\ \parallel \\ CH_3\text{—C—}CH_3 \end{matrix}$		
$\begin{matrix} H \\ \mid \\ CH_3\text{—N—}CH_3 \end{matrix}$		

Report Sheet

Questions and Problems

Q.4 Classify the following organic compounds according to their functional groups:

a. _____ $CH_3-CH_2-CH=CH-CH_3$

b. _____ $CH_3-CH_2-\overset{\overset{\displaystyle H}{|}}{N}-CH_2-CH_3$

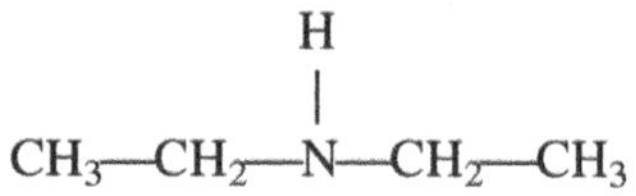

c. _____ $CH_3-CH_2-O-CH_3$

d. _____ $CH_3-\overset{\overset{\displaystyle O}{\|}}{C}-CH_2-CH_3$

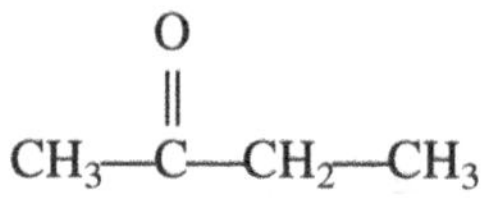

e. _____ $CH_3-CH_2-CH_2-\overset{\overset{\displaystyle O}{\|}}{C}-OH$

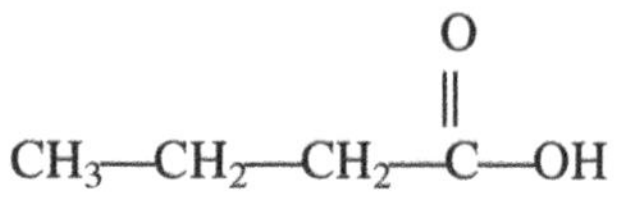

f. _____ $CH_3-CH_2-CH_2-\overset{\overset{\displaystyle O}{\|}}{C}-O-CH_3$

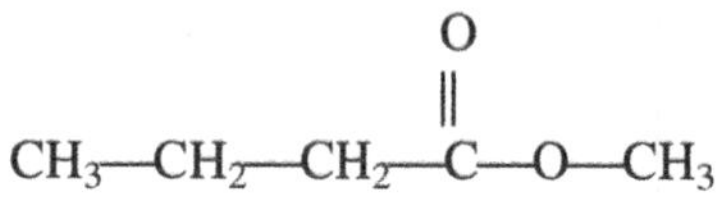

Goals

- Draw formulas for alkanes from their three-dimensional models.
- Write the names of alkanes from their structural formulas.
- Construct models of isomers of alkanes.
- Write the structural formulas for cycloalkanes and haloalkanes.

Discussion

A. Structures of Alkanes

The saturated hydrocarbons represent a group of organic compounds composed of carbon and hydrogen. Alkanes and cycloalkanes are called *saturated* hydrocarbons because their carbon atoms are connected by only single bonds. In each type of alkane, each carbon atom has four valence electrons and must always have four single bonds.

To learn more about the three-dimensional structure of organic compounds, it is helpful to build models using a ball-and-stick model kit. In the kit are wooden (or plastic) balls, which represent the typical elements in organic compounds. Each wooden atom has the correct number of holes drilled for bonds that attach to other atoms. See Table 1.

Table 1 *Elements and Bonds Represented in the Organic Model Kit*

Color	Element	Number of Bonds
Black	carbon	4
Yellow	hydrogen	1
Red	oxygen	2
Green	chlorine	1
Orange	bromine	1
Purple	iodine	1
Blue	nitrogen	3
Bonds		
Sticks, springs		

The first model to build is methane, CH_4, a hydrocarbon consisting of one carbon atom and four hydrogen atoms. The model of methane shows the three-dimensional shape, a tetrahedron, around a carbon atom.

| Three-dimensional structure | Complete structural formula | Condensed structural formula |

To represent this model on paper, its shape is flattened, and the carbon atom is shown attached to four hydrogen atoms. This type of formula is called a *complete structural formula.* However, it is more convenient to use a shortened version called a *condensed structural formula.* To write a condensed formula, the hydrogen atoms are grouped with their carbon atom. The number of hydrogen atoms is written as a subscript. The complete structural formula and the condensed structural formula for C_2H_6 are shown below:

$$H-\overset{\displaystyle H}{\underset{\displaystyle H}{C}}-\overset{\displaystyle H}{\underset{\displaystyle H}{C}}-H$$

$$CH_3-CH_3 \quad \text{or} \quad CH_3CH_3$$

Complete structural formula   Condensed structural formula

Names of Alkanes

The names of alkanes all end with -*ane.* The names of organic compounds are based on the names of the alkane family. See Table 2.

Table 2 *Names and Formulas of the First Ten Alkanes*

Name	Formula	Name	Formula
Methane	CH_4	Hexane	$CH_3CH_2CH_2CH_2CH_2CH_3$
Ethane	CH_3CH_3	Heptane	$CH_3CH_2CH_2CH_2CH_2CH_2CH_3$
Propane	$CH_3CH_2CH_3$	Octane	$CH_3CH_2CH_2CH_2CH_2CH_2CH_2CH_3$
Butane	$CH_3CH_2CH_2CH_3$	Nonane	$CH_3CH_2CH_2CH_2CH_2CH_2CH_2CH_2CH_3$
Pentane	$CH_3CH_2CH_2CH_2CH_3$	Decane	$CH_3CH_2CH_2CH_2CH_2CH_2CH_2CH_2CH_2CH_3$

B. Constitutional Isomers

Constitutional Isomers are present when a molecular formula can represent two or more different structural (or condensed) formulas. One structure cannot be converted to the other without breaking and forming new bonds. The isomers have different physical and chemical properties. One of the reasons for the vast array of organic compounds is the phenomenon of isomerism.

Isomers of C_4H_{10}

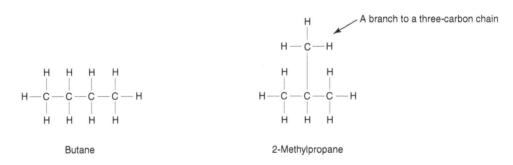

Butane   2-Methylpropane

138

C. Cycloalkanes

In a cycloalkane, an alkane has a cyclic or ring structure. There are no end carbon atoms. The structural formula of a cycloalkane indicates all of the carbon and hydrogen atoms. The condensed formula groups the hydrogen atoms with each of the carbon atoms. Another type of notation called the *geometric* structure is often used to depict a cycloalkane by showing only the bonds that outline the geometric shape of the compound. For example, the geometric shape of cyclopropane is a triangle, and the geometric shape of cyclobutane is a square. Examples of the various structural formulas for cyclobutane are shown below.

$$
\begin{array}{cc}
H & H \\
| & | \\
H-C-C-H \\
| & | \\
H-C-C-H \\
| & | \\
H & H
\end{array}
\qquad
\begin{array}{cc}
H_2C - CH_2 \\
| & | \\
H_2C - CH_2
\end{array}
\qquad
\square
$$

Complete structural formula   Condensed formula   Geometric formula

D. Haloalkanes

In a haloalkane, a halogen atom such as chlorine (Cl) or bromine (Br) replaces a hydrogen atom of an alkane or a cycloalkane.

Complete Structural Formula	Condensed Formula	Name
$\begin{array}{c} H \\ \| \\ H-C-Cl \\ \| \\ H \end{array}$	CH_3Cl	Chloromethane (methyl chloride)
$\begin{array}{cc} H & H \\ \| & \| \\ Br-C-C-Br \\ \| & \| \\ H & H \end{array}$	$BrCH_2CH_2Br$	1,2-Dibromoethane

Lab Information

Time: 2 hr
Comments: Tear out the report sheets and place them next to the matching procedures.
Related Topics: Alkane, cycloalkane, haloalkane, complete structural formula, condensed structural formula, constitutional isomers, naming alkanes

Experimental Procedures

A. Structures of Alkanes

Wear your safety goggles!

Materials: Organic model kit

A.1 Using an organic model kit, construct a ball-and-stick model of a molecule of methane, CH_4. Place wooden dowels in all the holes in the carbon atom (black). Attach hydrogen (yellow) atoms to each. Draw the three-dimensional (tetrahedral) shape of methane. Write the complete structural formula and the condensed structural formula of methane.

A.2 Make a model of ethane, C_2H_6. Observe that the tetrahedral shape is maintained for each carbon atom in the structure. Write the complete structural and condensed structural formulas for ethane.

A.3 Make a model of propane, C_3H_8. Write the complete structural and condensed structural formulas for propane.

B. Constitutional Isomers

Materials: Organic model kit, chemistry handbook

B.1 The molecular formula of butane is C_4H_{10}. Construct a model of butane by connecting four carbon atoms in a chain. Draw its complete and condensed structural formulas.

B.2 Make an isomer of C_4H_{10}. Remove an end -CH_3 group and attach it to the center carbon atom. Complete the end of the chain with a hydrogen atom. Write its complete and condensed structural formulas.

B.3 Obtain a chemistry handbook. For each isomer, find the molar mass, melting point, boiling point, and density.

B.4 Make models of the three isomers of C_5H_{12}. Make the continuous-chain isomer first. Draw the complete structural and condensed structural formulas for each. Name each isomer.

B.5 Obtain a chemistry handbook, and find the molar mass, melting point, boiling point, and density of each structural isomer.

C. Cycloalkanes

Materials: Organic model kit

C.1 Use the springs in the model kits to make a model of the cycloalkane with three carbon atoms. Write the complete structural and condensed structural formulas. Draw the geometric formula and name this compound.

C.2 Use the springs in the model kits to make models of a cycloalkane with four carbon atoms, and one with five carbon atoms. Draw the complete structural and condensed structural formulas. Draw the geometric formula and give the name for each.

D. Haloalkanes

Materials: Organic model kit

D.1 Make a model of chloromethane using a green wooden ball for chlorine. Draw the complete structural and condensed structural formulas.

D.2 Make a model of 1,2-dibromoethane using orange wooden balls for the bromine atoms. Draw the complete structural and condensed structural formulas.

D.3 Make a model of 2-iodopropane using a violet wooden ball for iodine. Draw the complete structural and condensed structural formulas.

D.4 Prepare models of four isomers of dichloropropane. Draw the complete structural and condensed structural formulas. Name each isomer.

Report Sheet

Date _____   Name _____

Section _____   Team _____

Instructor _____

Pre-Lab Study Questions

1. What elements are present in alkanes?

2. How does a complete structural formula differ from a condensed structural formula?

3. If isomers of an alkane have the same molecular formula, how do they differ?

A.   Structures of Alkanes

A.1 **Structure of methane**		
Tetrahedral shape	Complete structural formula	Condensed structural formula

A.2 **Structure of ethane**	
Complete structural formula	Condensed structural formula

A.3 **Structure of propane**	
Complete structural formula	Condensed structural formula

Report Sheet

Questions and Problems

Q.1 Write the correct name of the following alkanes:

a. $CH_3CH_2CH_3$ _____

b. 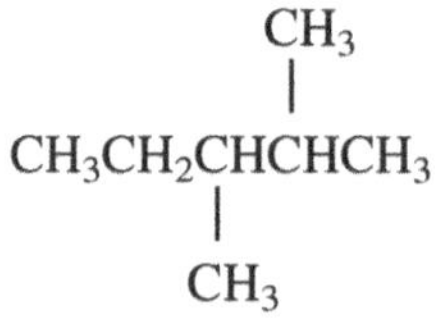
$$CH_3CH_2\overset{\overset{\displaystyle CH_3}{\displaystyle |}}{C}H\overset{\overset{\displaystyle }{\displaystyle }}{\underset{\underset{\displaystyle CH_3}{\displaystyle |}}{C}}HCH_3$$ _____

c.
$$CH_3-\overset{\overset{\displaystyle CH_3}{\displaystyle |}}{C}H-\overset{\overset{\displaystyle CH_3}{\displaystyle |}}{C}H-CH_3$$ _____

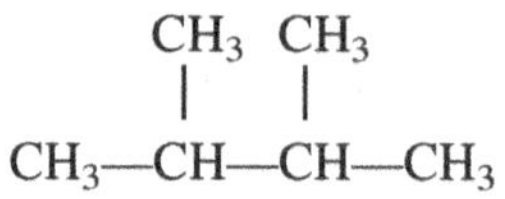

Q.2 Write the condensed formulas for the following:

a. hexane   b. 2,3-dimethylpentane

B. Constitutional Isomers

B.1 Butane C_4H_{10}	
Complete structural formula	Condensed structural formula
B.2 2-Methylpropane	
Complete structural formula	Condensed structural formul

142

Report Sheet

B.3 Physical Properties of Isomers of C_4H_{10}				
Isomer	Molar Mass	Melting Point	Boiling Point	Density
Butane				
2-Methylpropane (isobutane)				

Questions and Problems

Q.3   In B.3, what physical property is identical for the two isomers of C_4H_{10}?

Q.4   What physical properties are different for the isomers? Explain.

Report Sheet

B.4 Isomers of C_5H_{12}	
Complete structural formula	Condensed structural formula
Name:	
Complete structural formula	Condensed structural formula
Name:	
Complete structural formula	Condensed structural formula
Name:	

B.5 Physical Properties of Isomers of C_5H_{12}				
Isomer	**Molar Mass**	**Melting Point**	**Boiling Point**	**Density**
Pentane				
2-Methylbutane				
2,2-Dimethylpropane				

Report Sheet

Questions and Problems

Q.5 Write the condensed formulas for the five isomers of C_6H_{14}.

C. Cycloalkanes

Complete Structural Formula	Condensed Structural Formula	Geometric Formula
	C.1 Three carbon atoms	
Name:		
	C.2 Four carbon atoms	
Name:		
	Five carbon atoms	
Name:		

Report Sheet

D. Haloalkanes

Complete Structural Formula	Condensed Structural Formula
D.1 Chloromethane	
D.2 1,2-Dibromoethane	
D.3 2-Iodopropane	

Report Sheet

D.4 Four isomers of dichloropropane

Complete Structural Formula	Condensed Structural Formula
Name:	
Name:	
Name:	
Name:	

Report Sheet

Questions and Problems

Q.6 Write the condensed structural formulas and names for all the constitutional isomers with the formula C_4H_9Cl.

Goals

- Identify the characteristic functional groups of carbohydrates.
- Describe common carbohydrates and their sources.
- Distinguish between monosaccharides, disaccharides, and polysaccharides.

Discussion

Carbohydrates in our diet are our major source of energy. Foods high in carbohydrates include potatoes, bread, pasta, and rice. If we take in more carbohydrate than we need for energy, the excess is converted to fat, which can lead to a weight gain. The carbohydrate family is organized into three classes, which are the monosaccharides, disaccharides, and polysaccharides.

A. Monosaccharides

Monosaccharides contain C, H, and O in units of $(CH_2O)_n$. Most common monosaccharides have six carbon atoms (hexoses) with a general formula of $C_6H_{12}O_6$. They contain many hydroxyl groups (–OH) along with a carbonyl group. The aldoses are monosaccharides with an aldehyde group, and ketoses contain a ketone group.

Monosaccharides		Sources
Glucose	$C_6H_{12}O_6$	Fruit juices, honey, corn syrup
Galactose	$C_6H_{12}O_6$	Lactose hydrolysis
Fructose	$C_6H_{12}O_6$	Fruit juices, honey, sucrose hydrolysis

Glucose, a hexose, is the most common monosaccharide; it is also known as blood sugar.

$$
\begin{array}{c}
O \\
\parallel \\
C-H \\
\mid \\
H-C-OH \\
\mid \\
HO-C-H \\
\mid \\
H-C-OH \\
\mid \\
H-C-OH \\
\mid \\
CH_2OH
\end{array}
$$

D-Glucose

The letter D refers to the orientation of the hydroxyl group on the chiral carbon that is farthest from the carbonyl group at the top of the chain (carbon 1). The D- and L-isomers of glyceraldehyde illustrate the position of the –OH on the central, chiral atom.

From *Laboratory Manual for General, Organic, & Biological Chemistry*, Karen C. Timberlake. Copyright © 2002 Pearson Education, Inc., publishing as Benjamin Cummings. All rights reserved.

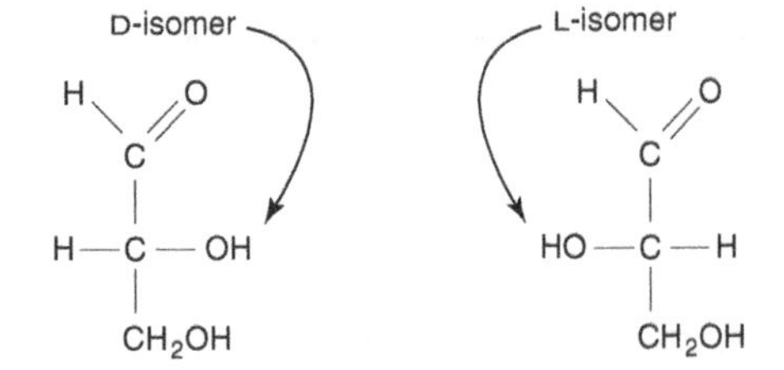

D-Glyceraldehyde   L-Glyceraldehyde

Haworth Structures

Most of the time glucose exists in a ring structure, which forms when the OH on carbon 5 forms a hemiacetal bond with the aldehyde group. In the Haworth structure the new hydroxyl group on carbon 1 may be drawn above carbon 1 (the β form) or below carbon 1 (the α form).

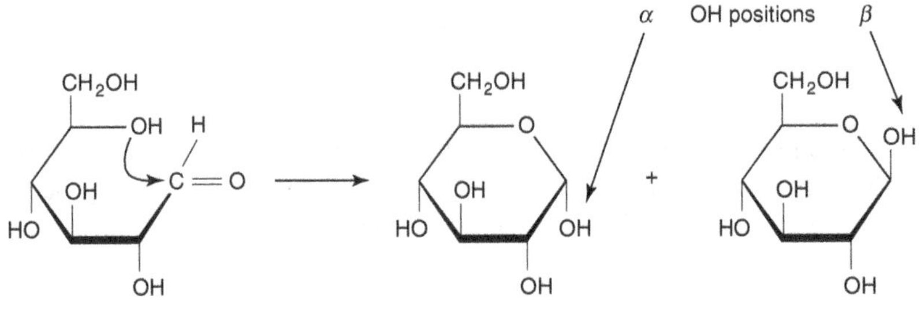

D-Glucose α-D-Glucose β-D-Glucose

B. Disaccharides

The disaccharides contain two of the common monosaccharides. Some common disaccharides include maltose, sucrose (table sugar), and lactose (milk sugar).

Disaccharides	Sources	Monosaccharides
Maltose	Germinating grains, starch hydrolysis	Glucose + glucose
Lactose	Milk, yogurt, ice cream	Glucose + galactose
Sucrose	Sugar cane, sugar beets	Glucose + fructose

In a disaccharide, two monosaccharides form a glycosidic bond with the loss of water. For example, in maltose, two glucose units are linked by an α-1,4-glycosidic bond.

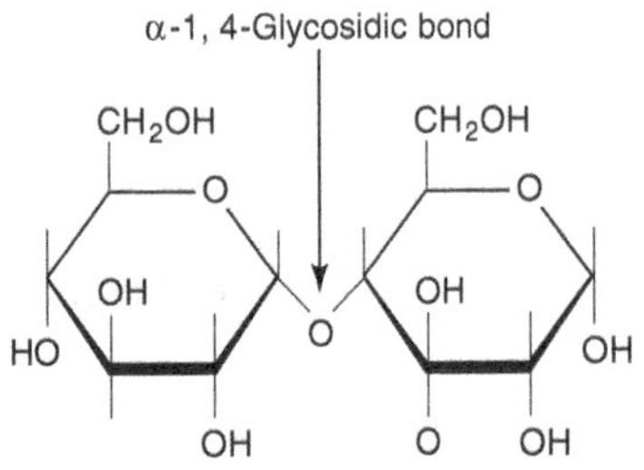

α-Maltose

C. Polysaccharides

Polysaccharides are long-chain polymers that contain many thousands of monosaccharides (usually glucose units) joined together by glycosidic bonds. Three important polysaccharides are starch, cellulose, and glycogen. They all contain glucose units, but differ in the type of glycosidic bonds and the amount of branching in the molecule.

Polysaccharides	Found in	Monosaccharides
Starch (amylose, amylopectin)	Rice, wheat, grains, cereals	Glucose
Glycogen	Muscle, liver	Glucose
Cellulose	Wood, plants, paper, cotton	Glucose

Starch is an insoluble storage form of glucose found in rice, wheat, potatoes, beans, and cereals. Starch is composed of two kinds of polysaccharides, amylose and amylopectin. *Amylose*, which makes up about 20% of starch, consists of α-D-glucose molecules connected by α-1,4-glycosidic bonds in a continuous chain. A typical polymer of amylose may contain from 250 to 4000 glucose units.

α-1,4-Glycosidic bonds in amylose

Amylopectin is a branched-chain polysaccharide that makes up as much as 80% of starch. In amylopectin, α-1,4-glycosidic bonds connect most of the glucose molecules. However, at about every 25 glucose units, there are branches of glucose molecules attached by α-1,6-glycosidic bonds between carbon 1 of the branch and carbon 6 in the main chain.

Amylopectin

Glycogen is a similar to amylopectin but it is even more highly branched, with α-1,6-glycosidic bonds about every 10-15 glucose units.

Cellulose is the major structural material of wood and plants. Cotton is almost pure cellulose. In cellulose, glucose molecules form a long unbranched chain similar to amylose except that β-1,4-glycosidic bonds connect the glucose molecules. The β isomers are aligned in parallel rows that are held in place by hydrogen bonds between the rows. This gives a rigid structure for cell walls in wood and fiber and makes cellulose more resistant to hydrolysis.

Cellulose

Lab Information

Time: 2 hr

Comments: Tear out the report sheets and place them next to the matching procedures.
In the study of carbohydrates, it is helpful to review stereoisomers and the formation of hemiacetals.

Related Topics: Carbohydrates, monosaccharides, disaccharides, polysaccharides, hemiacetals, stereoisomers, aldohexoses, ketohexoses, chiral compounds, Fischer projection, Haworth structures

Experimental Procedures

A. Monosaccharides

Materials: Organic model kits or prepared models

A.1   Make or observe models of L-glyceraldehyde and D-glyceraldehyde. Draw the Fischer projections.

A.2   Draw the Fischer projection for D-glucose. Draw the Haworth (cyclic) formulas for the α and β anomers.

A.3   Draw the Fischer projections for D-fructose and D-galactose. Draw the Haworth (cyclic) formulas for the α anomers of each.

B. Disaccharides

B.1   Using Haworth formulas, write the structure for α-D-maltose. Look at a model if available.

B.2   Write an equation for the hydrolysis of α-D-maltose by adding H_2O to the glycosidic bond.

B.3   Using Haworth formulas, write an equation for the formation of α-D-lactose from β-D-galactose and α-D-glucose.

B.4   Draw the structure of sucrose and circle the glycosidic bond.

C. Polysaccharides

C.1   Draw a portion of amylose using four units of α-D-glucose. Indicate the glycosidic bonds.

C.2   Describe how the structure of amylopectin differs from the structure of amylose.

C.3   Draw a portion of cellulose using four units of β-D-glucose. Indicate the glycosidic bonds.

152

Report Sheet

Date _____   Name _____

Section _____   Team _____

Instructor _____

Pre-Lab Study Questions

1.   What are some sources of carbohydrates in your diet?

2.   What does the D in D-glucose mean?

3.   What is the bond that links monosaccharides in di- and polysaccharides?

A.   Monosaccharides

A.1 Fischer projections

L-glyceraldehyde   D-glyceraldehyde

How does L-glyceraldehyde differ from D-glyceraldehyde?

A.2 Fischer projection of D-glucose   Haworth (cyclic) formulas

α-D-glucose β-D-glucose

Report Sheet

A.3 Fischer projection of D-fructose   Haworth (cyclic) formula for α-D-fructose

Fischer projection of D-galactose   Haworth (cyclic) formula for α-D-galactose

Questions and Problems

Q.1 How does the structure of D-glucose compare to the structure of D-galactose?

B. Disaccharides

B.1 Structure of α-D-maltose

B.2 Equation for the hydrolysis of α-D-maltose

Report Sheet

B.3   Formation of α-D-lactose

B.4   Structure of sucrose

Questions and Problems

Q.2   What is the type of glycosidic bond in maltose?

Q.3   Why does maltose have both α and β anomers? Explain.

C.   Polysaccharides

C.1   A portion of amylose

C.2   Comparison of amylopectin to amylose

Report Sheet

C.3   A portion of cellulose

Questions and Problems

Q.4   What is the monosaccharide that results from the complete hydrolysis of amylose?

Q.5   What is the difference in the structure of amylose and cellulose?

Goals

- Observe physical and chemical properties of some common carbohydrates.
- Use physical and chemical tests to distinguish between monosaccharides, disaccharides, and polysaccharides.
- Identify an unknown carbohydrate.
- Relate the process of digestion to the hydrolysis of carbohydrates.

Discussion

A. Benedict's Test for Reducing Sugars

All of the monosaccharides and most of the disaccharides can be oxidized. When the cyclic structure opens, the aldehyde group is available for oxidation. Benedict's reagent contains Cu^{2+} ion that is reduced. Therefore, all the sugars that react with Benedict's reagent are called *reducing sugars*. Ketoses also act as reducing sugars because the ketone group on carbon 2 isomerizes to give an aldehyde group on carbon 1.

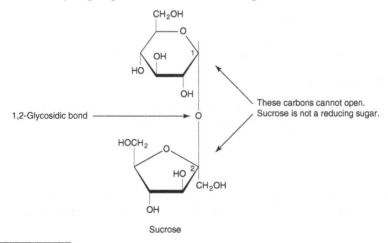

When oxidation of a sugar occurs, the Cu^{2+} is reduced to Cu^+, which forms a red precipitate of cuprous oxide, $Cu_2O(s)$. The color of the precipitate varies from green to gold to red depending on the concentration of the reducing sugar.

Sucrose is not a reducing sugar because it cannot revert to the open-chain form that would provide the aldehyde group needed to reduce the cupric ion.

From *Laboratory Manual for General, Organic, & Biological Chemistry,* Karen C. Timberlake. Copyright © 2002 Pearson Education, Inc., publishing as Benjamin Cummings. All rights reserved.

B. Seliwanoff's Test for Ketoses

Seliwanoff's test is used to distinguish between hexoses with a ketone group and hexoses that are aldehydes. With ketoses, a deep red color is formed rapidly. Aldoses give a light pink color that takes a longer time to develop. The test is most sensitive for fructose, which is a ketose.

C. Fermentation Test

Most monosaccharides and disaccharides undergo fermentation in the presence of yeast. The products of fermentation are ethyl alcohol (CH_3CH_2OH) and carbon dioxide (CO_2). The formation of bubbles of carbon dioxide is used to confirm the fermentation process.

$$\underset{\text{Glucose}}{C_6H_{12}O_6} \xrightarrow{\text{yeast}} \underset{\text{Ethanol}}{2C_2H_5OH} + 2CO_2(g)$$

Although enzymes are present for the hydrolysis of most disaccharides, they are not available for lactose. The enzymes needed for the fermentation of galactose are not present in yeast. Lactose and galactose give negative results with the fermentation test.

D. Iodine Test for Polysaccharides

When iodine (I_2) is added to amylose, the helical shape of the unbranched polysaccharide traps iodine molecules, producing a deep blue-black complex. Amylopectin, cellulose, and glycogen react with iodine to give red to brown colors. Glycogen produces a reddish-purple color. Monosaccharides and disaccharides are too small to trap iodine molecules and do not form dark colors with iodine.

E. Hydrolysis of Disaccharides and Polysaccharides

Disaccharides hydrolyze in the presence of an acid to give the individual monosaccharides.

$$\text{Sucrose} + H_2O \xrightarrow{H^+} \text{Glucose} + \text{Fructose}$$

In the laboratory, we use water and acid to hydrolyze starches, which produce smaller saccharides such as maltose. Eventually, the hydrolysis reaction converts maltose to glucose molecules. In the body, enzymes in our saliva and from the pancreas carry out the hydrolysis. Complete hydrolysis produces glucose, which provides about 50% of our nutritional calories.

$$\text{Amylose, amylopectin} \xrightarrow[\text{amylase}]{H^+ \text{ or}} \text{dextrins} \xrightarrow[\text{amylase}]{H^+ \text{ or}} \text{maltose} \xrightarrow[\text{maltase}]{H^+ \text{ or}} \text{many D-glucose units}$$

F. Testing Foods for Carbohydrates

Several of the tests such as the iodine test can be carried out with food products such as cereals, bread, crackers, and pasta. Some of the carbohydrates we have discussed can be identified.

Lab Information

Time: 3 hr
Comments: Tear out the report sheets and place them next to the matching procedures. .
Related Topics: Carbohydrates, hemiacetals, aldohexoses, ketohexoses, reducing sugars, fermentation

Experimental Procedures

A. Benedict's Test for Reducing Sugars

Materials: Test tubes, 400-mL beaker, droppers, hot plate or Bunsen burner, 5- or 10-mL graduated cylinder, Benedict's reagent, 2% carbohydrate solutions: glucose, fructose, sucrose, lactose, starch, and an unknown

Place 10 drops of solutions of glucose, fructose, sucrose, lactose, starch, water, and unknown in separate test tubes. Label each test tube. Add 2 mL of Benedict's reagent to each sample. Place the test tubes in a boiling water bath for 3–4 minutes. The formation of a greenish to reddish-orange color indicates the presence of a reducing sugar. If the solution is the same color as the Benedict's reagent in water (the control), there has been no oxidation reaction. Record your observations. Classify each as a reducing or nonreducing sugar.

B. Seliwanoff's Test for Ketoses

Materials: Test tubes, 400-mL beaker, droppers, hot plate or Bunsen burner, 5- or 10-mL graduated cylinder, Seliwanoff's reagent, 2% carbohydrate solutions: glucose, fructose, sucrose, lactose, starch, and an unknown

Place 10 drops of solutions of glucose, fructose, sucrose, lactose, starch, water, and unknown in separate test tubes. Add 2 mL of Seliwanoff's reagent to each. ***The reagent contains concentrated HCl. Use carefully.***

Place the test tubes in a boiling hot water bath and note the time. After 1 minute, observe the colors in the test tubes. A rapid formation of a deep red color indicates the presence of a ketose. Record your results as a fast color change, slow change, or no change.

C. Fermentation Test

Materials: Fermentation tubes (or small and large test tubes), baker's yeast, 2% carbohydrate solutions: glucose, fructose, sucrose, lactose, starch, and an unknown

Fill fermentation tubes with a solution of glucose, fructose, sucrose, lactose, starch, water, and unknown. Add 0.2 g of yeast to each and mix well. See Figure 1.

Figure 1   Fermentation tube filled with a carbohydrate solution

If fermentation tubes are not available, use small test tubes placed upside down in larger test tubes. Cover the mouth of the large test tube with filter paper or cardboard. Place your hand firmly over the paper cover and invert. When the small test tube inside has completely filled with the mixture, return the larger test tube to an upright position. See Figure 2.

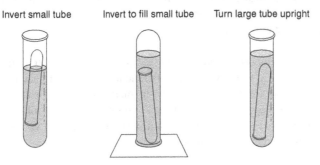

Invert small tube   Invert to fill small tube   Turn large tube upright

Figure 2   Test tubes used as fermentation tubes

Set the tubes aside. At the end of the laboratory period, and again at the next laboratory period, look for gas bubbles in the fermentation tubes or inside the small tubes. Record your observations. See Figure 3.

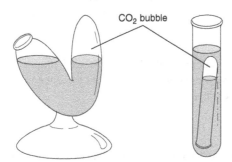

CO₂ bubble

Figure 3   Fermentation tubes with CO₂ bubbles

D. Iodine Test for Polysaccharides

Materials: Spot plate or test tubes, droppers, iodine reagent, 2% carbohydrate solutions in dropper bottles: glucose, fructose, sucrose, lactose, starch, and an unknown

Using a spot plate, place 5 drops of each solution of glucose, fructose, sucrose, lactose, starch, water, and unknown in the wells. (If you do not have a spot plate, use small test tubes.) Add 1 drop of iodine solution to each sample. A dark blue-black color is a positive test for amylose in starch. A red or brown color indicates the presence of other polysaccharides. Record your results. Complete the table to identify your unknown.

E. Hydrolysis of Disaccharides and Polysaccharides

Materials: Test tubes, 10-mL graduated cylinder, 400-mL beaker (boiling water bath), hot plate or Bunsen burner, spot plate or watch glass, 10% HCl, 10% NaOH, red litmus paper, iodine reagent, Benedict's reagent, 2% starch and sucrose solutions in dropper bottles

Place 3 mL of 2% starch in two test tubes and 3 mL of 2% sucrose solution in two more test tubes. To one sample each of sucrose and starch, add 20 drops of 10% HCl. To the other samples of sucrose and starch, add 20 drops of H_2O. Label the test tubes and heat in a boiling water bath for 10 minutes.

Remove the test tubes from the water bath and let them cool. To the samples containing HCl, add 10% NaOH (about 20 drops) until one drop of the mixture turns litmus paper blue, indicating the HCl has been neutralized. Test the samples for hydrolysis as follows:

Iodine Test Place 5 drops of each solution on a spot plate or watch glass. Add 1 drop of iodine reagent to each. Record observations. Determine if hydrolysis has occurred in each.

Benedict's Test Add 2 mL of Benedict's reagent to each of the samples and heat in a boiling water bath for 3–4 minutes. Determine if hydrolysis has occurred in each.

F.   Testing Foods for Carbohydrates

Materials: Sugar samples (refined, brown, "natural," powdered), honey, syrups (corn, maple, fruit), foods with starches: cereals, pasta, bread, crackers, potato, Benedict's solution, Seliwanoff's reagent, iodine reagent

Obtain two carbohydrate samples to test. Perform the Benedict's, Seliwanoff's, and iodine tests on each. Describe the kinds of carbohydrates you identify in each sample.

Report Sheet

Date _____   Name _____

Section _____   Team _____

Instructor _____

Pre-Lab Study Questions

1. What happens to glucose or galactose when the Cu^{2+} in Benedict's is reduced?

2. Would you expect fructose or glucose to form a red color rapidly with Seliwanoff's reagent?

3. Why don't all the disaccharides undergo fermentation with yeast?

4. How can the iodine test be used to distinguish between amylose and glycogen?

Results of Carbohydrate Tests

	A. Benedict's Test	B. Seliwanoff's Test	C. Fermentation Test	D. Iodine Test
Glucose				
Fructose				
Sucrose				
Lactose				
Starch				
Water				
Unknown #_____				

Report Sheet

Questions and Problems

Q.1 From the results in part A, list the sugars that are reducing sugars and those that are not.

Reducing sugars

Nonreducing sugars

Q.2 What sugars are ketoses?

Q.3 What sugars give a positive fermentation test?

Q.4 Which carbohydrates give a blue-black color in the iodine test?

Identifying an Unknown Carbohydrate

Unknown No._____

	Results with Unknown	Possible Sugars Present
Benedict's (A)		
Seliwanoff's (B)		
Fermentation (C)		
Iodine (D)		

What carbohydrate(s) is/are in your unknown?

Report Sheet

Questions and Problems

Q.5 What carbohydrate(s) would have the following test results?
   a. Produces a reddish-orange solid with Benedict's and a red color with Seliwanoff's reagent in 1 minute

   b. Gives a color change with Benedict's test, a light orange color with Seliwanoff's reagent after 5 minutes, and produces no bubbles during fermentation

   c. Gives no color change with Benedict's or Seliwanoff's test, but turns a blue-black color with iodine reagent

E.   Results of Carbohydrate Tests

Results	Sucrose + H_2O	Sucrose + HCl	Starch + H_2O	Starch + HCl
Iodine test				
Benedict's test				
Hydrolysis products present				

Questions and Problems

Q.6 How do the results of the Benedict's test indicate that hydrolysis of sucrose and starch occurred?

Q.7 How do the results of the iodine test indicate that hydrolysis of starch occurred?

Report Sheet

Q.8   Indicate whether the following carbohydrates will give a positive (+) or a negative (-) result in each type of test listed below:

	Benedict's Test	Seliwanoff's Test	Fermentation Test	Iodine Test
Glucose				
Fructose				
Galactose				
Sucrose				
Lactose				
Maltose				
Amylose				
Amylopectin				

F.   Testing Foods for Carbohydrates

	Food Item 1	Food Item 2
Benedict's test		
Seliwanoff's test		
Iodine test		
Possible carbohydrates present		

Goals

- Observe the physical and chemical properties of some common lipids.
- Draw the structure of a typical triacylglycerol.
- Distinguish between saturated and unsaturated fats.
- Determine the degree of unsaturation of some fats.
- Prepare a hand lotion and determine the function of its components.

Discussion

A. Triacylglycerols

The triacylglycerols, commonly called fats or oils, are esters of glycerol and fatty acids. Fatty acids are long-chain carboxylic acids, usually 14 to 18 carbons in length. When the fatty acid contains double bonds, the triacylglycerol is referred to as an unsaturated fat. When the fatty acid consists of an alkane-like carbon chain, the triacylglycerol is a saturated fat. Table 1 gives the formulas of the common fatty acids and their melting points. At room temperature, saturated fats are usually solid and unsaturated fats are usually liquid.

Table 1 *Formulas, Melting Points, and Sources of Some Fatty Acids*

Carbon Atoms	Structural Formula	Melting Point (°C)	Common Name	Source
Saturated fatty acids (single carbon–carbon bonds)				
12	$CH_3(CH_2)_{10}COOH$	44	lauric	coconut
14	$CH_3(CH_2)_{12}COOH$	54	myristic	nutmeg
16	$CH_3(CH_2)_{14}COOH$	63	palmitic	palm
18	$CH_3(CH_2)_{16}COOH$	70	stearic	animal fat
Monounsaturated fatty acids (one cis double bond)				
16	$CH_3(CH_2)_5CH=CH(CH_2)_7COOH$	1	palmitoleic	butter fat
18	$CH_3(CH_2)_7CH=CH(CH_2)_7COOH$	4	oleic	olives, corn
Polyunsaturated fatty acids (two or more cis double bonds)				
18	$CH_3(CH_2)_4CH=CHCH_2CH=CH(CH_2)_7COOH$	-5	linoleic	safflower, sunflower
18	$CH_3CH_2CH=CHCH_2CH=CHCH_2CH=CH(CH_2)_7COOH$	-11	linolenic	corn

Fats that contain mostly saturated fatty acids have a higher melting point than fats with more unsaturated fatty acids.

$$
\begin{array}{l}
CH_2\text{—}OH \\
| \\
CH\text{—}OH \\
| \\
CH_2\text{—}OH
\end{array}
\; + \;
\begin{array}{l}
\overset{O}{\overset{\|}{HO\text{—}C(CH_2)_{14}CH_3}} \\
\overset{O}{\overset{\|}{HO\text{—}C(CH_2)_{14}CH_3}} \\
\overset{O}{\overset{\|}{HO\text{—}C(CH_2)_{14}CH_3}}
\end{array}
\longrightarrow
\begin{array}{l}
\overset{O}{\overset{\|}{CH_2\text{—}O\text{—}C(CH_2)_{14}CH_3}} \\
\overset{O}{\overset{\|}{CH\text{—}O\text{—}C(CH_2)_{14}CH_3}} \\
\overset{O}{\overset{\|}{CH_2\text{—}O\text{—}C(CH_2)_{14}CH_3}}
\end{array}
\; + \; 3\,H_2O
$$

Glycerol   3 Palmitic acids   Glyceryl palmitate (tripalmitin)

B. Physical Properties of Some Lipids and Fatty Acids

Lipids are a family of compounds that are grouped by similarities in solubility rather than structure. As a group, lipids are more soluble in nonpolar solvents such as ether, chloroform, or benzene. Most are not soluble in water. Important types of lipids include fats and oils, glycerophospholipids, and steroids. Compounds classified as lipids include fat-soluble vitamins A, D, E, and K; cholesterol; hormones; portions of cell membranes; and vegetable oils. Table 2 lists the classes of lipids.

Table 2   *Classes of Lipid Molecules*

Lipids	Components
Waxes	Fatty acid and long-chain alcohol
Fats and oils (triacylglycerols)	Fatty acids and glycerol
Glycerophospholipids	Fatty acids, glycerol, phosphate, amino alcohol
Sphingolipids	Fatty acids, sphingosine, phosphate, amino alcohol
Glycosphinolipids	Fatty acids, glycerophospholipids sphingosine, monosaccharides
Steroids	A fused structure of three cyclohexanes and a cyclopentane

The structural formulas of three typical lipids are shown below:

$$
\overset{O}{\overset{\|}{CH_3\text{—}(CH_2)_{14}\text{—}C\text{—}O\text{—}(CH_2)_{29}\text{—}CH_3}}
$$

Wax

$$
\begin{array}{l}
\overset{O}{\overset{\|}{CH_2\text{—}O\text{—}C\text{—}(CH_2)_{16}\text{—}CH_3}} \\
\overset{O}{\overset{\|}{CH\text{—}O\text{—}C\text{—}(CH_2)_{16}\text{—}CH_3}} \\
\overset{O}{\overset{\|}{CH_2\text{—}O\text{—}C\text{—}(CH_2)_{16}\text{—}CH_3}}
\end{array}
$$

Triacylglycerol, a fat

Cholesterol, a steroid

C. Bromine Test for Unsaturation

The presence of unsaturation in a fatty acid or a triacylglycerol can be detected by the bromine test, which you used in an earlier experiment to detect double bonds in alkenes. If the orange color of the bromine solution fades quickly, an addition reaction has occurred and the oil or fat is unsaturated.

Bromine adds to the double bond

$$
\begin{array}{l}
\text{CH}_2\text{—O—}\overset{\displaystyle O}{\overset{\|}{\text{C}}}\text{(CH}_2)_7\text{CH}=\text{CH(CH}_2)_7\text{CH}_3 \\[2pt]
\quad\overset{\displaystyle O}{\overset{\|}{|}} \\
\text{CH—O—}\overset{\displaystyle O}{\overset{\|}{\text{C}}}\text{(CH}_2)_{16}\text{CH}_3 \qquad + \text{Br}_2 \longrightarrow \\[2pt]
\quad\overset{\displaystyle O}{\overset{\|}{|}} \\
\text{CH}_2\text{—O—}\overset{\displaystyle O}{\overset{\|}{\text{C}}}\text{(CH}_2)_{16}\text{CH}_3
\end{array}
$$

$$
\begin{array}{l}
\text{CH}_2\text{—O—}\overset{\displaystyle O}{\overset{\|}{\text{C}}}\text{(CH}_2)_7\overset{\text{Br}}{\overset{|}{\text{CH}}}\text{—}\overset{\text{Br}}{\overset{|}{\text{CH}}}\text{(CH}_2)_7\text{CH}_3 \\[2pt]
\quad\overset{\displaystyle O}{\overset{\|}{|}} \\
\text{CH—O—}\overset{\displaystyle O}{\overset{\|}{\text{C}}}\text{(CH}_2)_{16}\text{CH}_3 \\[2pt]
\quad\overset{\displaystyle O}{\overset{\|}{|}} \\
\text{CH}_2\text{—O—}\overset{\displaystyle O}{\overset{\|}{\text{C}}}\text{(CH}_2)_{16}\text{CH}_3
\end{array}
$$

D. Preparation of Hand Lotion

We use hand lotions and creams to soften our skin and reduce dryness. Typically, the formulation of a hand lotion consists of several components such as stearic acid, lanolin, triethanolamine, cetyl alcohol, glycerin (glycerol), water, and usually a fragrance. Lanolin from wool consists of a mixture of waxes.

Cetyl alcohol $\qquad$ $CH_3(CH_2)_{15}OH$

Stearic acid $\qquad$ $CH_3\text{—}(CH_2)_{16}\text{—}\overset{\displaystyle O}{\overset{\|}{C}}\text{—OH}$

Glycerol (glycerine) $\qquad$
$$
\begin{array}{l}
\text{CH}_2\text{—OH} \\
| \\
\text{CH—OH} \\
| \\
\text{CH}_2\text{—OH}
\end{array}
$$

Triethanolamine $\qquad$
$$
\text{HOCH}_2\text{CH}_2\text{—}\overset{\overset{\displaystyle \text{CH}_2\text{CH}_2\text{OH}}{|}}{\text{N}}\text{—CH}_2\text{CH}_2\text{OH}
$$

Because lipids are nonpolar, they protect and soften by preventing the loss of moisture from the skin. Some of the components help emulsify the polar and nonpolar ingredients. In this experiment, we will see how the physical and chemical properties of lipids are used to prepare a hand lotion.

Lab Information

Time: 3 hr

Comments: Bromine can cause severe chemical burns. Use carefully.
Tear out the Lab report sheets and place them beside the matching procedures.

Related topics: Fatty acids, saturated and unsaturated fatty acids, lipids, triglycerides

Experimental Procedures

BE SURE YOU ARE WEARING YOUR SAFETY GOGGLES!

A. Triacylglycerols

Materials: Organic model kits or models

A.1 Use an organic model kit or observe prepared models of a molecule of glycerol and three molecules of ethanoic acid. What are the functional groups on each? Draw their structures.

A.2 Form ester bonds between the hydroxy groups on glycerol and the carboxylic acid groups of the ethanoic acid molecules. In the process, three molecules of water are removed. Write an equation for the formation of the glyceryl ethanoate.

Carry out the reverse process, which is hydrolysis. Add the components of water to break the ester bond. Add an arrow to the equation to show the reverse direction for the hydrolysis reaction.

B. Physical Properties of Some Lipids and Fatty Acids

Materials: Test tubes and stoppers, dropper bottles or solids: stearic acid, oleic acid, olive oil, safflower oil, lecithin, cholesterol, vitamin A capsules, spatulas, CH_2Cl_2 (optional)

To seven separate test tubes, add 5 drops or the amount of solid lipid held on the tip of a spatula: stearic acid, oleic acid, olive oil, safflower oil, lecithin, cholesterol, vitamin A (puncture a capsule or use cod liver oil).

Appearance and Odor

B.1 Classify each as a triacylglycerol (fat or oil), fatty acid, steroid, or phospholipid.

B.2 Describe their appearance.

B.3 Describe their odors.

Solubility in a Polar Solvent *(May be a demonstration)*

B.4 Add about 2 mL of water to each of the test tubes. Stopper and shake each test tube. Record your observations.

Solubility in a Nonpolar Solvent *(Optional or demonstration)*

B.5 Place 5 drops, or a small amount of solid, of the following in separate test tubes: stearic acid, oleic oil, olive oil, safflower oil, lecithin, cholesterol, and vitamin A. Add 1 mL (20 drops) methylene chloride, CH_2Cl_2, to each sample. Record the solubility of the lipids. *Save the test tubes and samples of stearic acid oleic acid, olive oil and safflower oil for part C.*

C. Bromine Test for Unsaturation

Materials: Samples from B.5, 1% Br_2 in methylene chloride

To the samples from B.5, add 1% bromine solution drop by drop until a permanent red-orange color is obtained or until 20 drops have been added.

Caution: Avoid contact with bromine solution; it can cause painful burns. Do not breathe the fumes.

Record your observations. Determine if the red-orange color fades rapidly or persists.

D. Preparation of Hand Lotion

Materials: Stearic acid, cetyl alcohol, lanolin (anhydrous), triethanolamine, glycerol, ethanol, distilled water, fragrance (optional), commercial hand lotions, 10-mL graduated cylinder, 50-mL graduated cylinder, 50-mL or 100-mL beakers, thermometer, 100-mL beakers, 250-mL beaker for water bath, Bunsen burner, iron ring, wire screen, stirring rods, tongs, pH paper

Team project: D.1, D.2, and D.3 may be prepared by different teams in the lab.

D.1 Obtain the following substances and combine in two 50-mL or 100-mL beakers. Use a laboratory balance to weigh out the solid substances. Use a 10-mL graduated cylinder to measure small volumes, and a 50-mL graduated cylinder to measure larger volumes.

Beaker 1		**Beaker 2**	
Stearic acid	3 g	Glycerin	2 mL
Cetyl alcohol	1 g	Water	50 mL
Lanolin (anhydrous)	2 g		
Triethanolamine	1 mL		

Water bath: Fill a 250-mL beaker about 2/3 full of water. Place the beaker on an iron ring covered with a wire screen. Lower a second iron ring that fits around the 250-mL beaker to stabilize it. Turn on the Bunsen burner to heat the water.

Using a pair of crucible tongs, hold Beaker 1 (four ingredients) in the water bath and heat to 80°C or until all the compounds have melted. Remove.

Using a pair of crucible tongs, place Beaker 2 (two ingredients) in the same water bath and heat to 80°C.

While still warm, slowly pour the glycerol-water mixture from Beaker 2 into Beaker 1 (four ingredients) as you stir. Add 5.0 mL of ethanol and a few drops of fragrance, if desired. Continue to stir for 3-5 minutes until a smooth, creamy lotion is obtained. If the resulting product is too thick, add more warm water.

Describe the smoothness and appearance of the hand lotion.

D.2 Repeat the experiment, but omit the triethanolamine from Beaker 1. Compare the properties of the resulting hand lotion to the one obtained in D.1 and to commercial hand lotions.

D.3 Repeat the experiment, but omit the stearic acid from Beaker 1. Compare the properties and textures of the resulting hand lotion to the one obtained in D.1 and to commercial hand lotions.

D.4 Determine the pH of the hand lotions you and others in your lab have prepared along with any commercial hand lotions.

Report Sheet

Date _____   Name _____

Section _____   Team _____

Instructor _____

Pre-Lab Study Questions

1. What is the functional group in a triacylglycerol?

2. Write the structure of linolenic acid. Why is it an unsaturated fatty acid?

A.   Triacylglycerols

A.1   Structure of glycerol   Structure of ethanoic acid

A.2   Reversible equation for the esterification and hydrolysis of glyceryl ethanoate

Report Sheet

B. Physical Properties of Some Lipids and Fatty Acids

Lipid	B.1 Type of Lipid	B.2 Appearance	B.3 Odor	B.4 Soluble in Water?	B.5 Soluble in CH_2Cl_2?
Stearic acid					
Oleic acid					
Olive oil					
Safflower oil					
Lecithin					
Cholesterol					
Vitamin A					

Questions and Problems

Q.1 Why are the compounds in part B classified as lipids?

Q.2 What type of solvent is needed to remove an oil spot? Why?

Report Sheet

C. Bromine Test for Unsaturation

Compound	Drops of Bromine Solution	Saturated or Unsaturated?
Fatty acids		
Stearic acid		
Oleic acid		
Triacylglycerols		
Safflower oil		
Olive oil		

Questions and Problems

Q.3 a. Write the condensed structural formulas of stearic acid and oleic acid.

Stearic acid

Oleic acid

b. Which fatty acid is unsaturated?

c. The melting point of stearic acid is 70°C, and that of oleic acid is 4°C. Explain the difference.

d. From the results of experiment C, how can you tell which is more unsaturated, oleic acid or stearic acid?

D. Preparation of Hand Lotion

Descriptions of the hand lotions		
D.1	D.2 (without triethanolamine)	D.3 (without stearic acid)
D.4 pH of the hand lotions		
pH of commercial hand lotions		
Brand_____	Brand_____	Brand_____
pH _____	pH _____	pH _____

Questions and Problems

Q. 4   How does omitting triethanolamine affect the properties and appearance of the hand lotion?

Q. 5   How does omitting stearic acid affect the properties and appearance of the hand lotion?

Q. 6   What would be a reason to have triethaonolamine and stearic acid as ingredients in hand lotion?

Saponification and Soaps

Goals

- Prepare soap by the saponification of a fat or oil.
- Observe the reactions of soap with oil, $CaCl_2$, $MgCl_2$, and $FeCl_3$.

Discussion

A. Saponification: Preparation of Soap

For centuries, soaps have been made from animal fats and lye (NaOH), which was obtained by pouring water through wood ashes. The hydrolysis of a fat or oil by a base such as NaOH is called *saponification* and the salts of the fatty acids obtained are called *soaps*. The other product of hydrolysis is glycerol, which is soluble in water.

| Fat | Base | Glycerol | Soap |
| (tripalmitin) | | | (sodium palmitate) |

The fats that are most commonly used to make soap are lard and tallow from animal fat and coconut, palm, and olive oils from vegetables. Castile soap is made from olive oil. Soaps that float have air pockets. Soft soaps are made with KOH instead of NaOH to give potassium salts.

B. Properties of Soaps and Detergents

A soap molecule has a dual nature. The nonpolar carbon chain is hydrophobic and attracted to nonpolar substances such as grease. The polar head of the carboxylate salt is hydrophilic and attracted to water.

The dual polarity of a soap (salt of a fatty acid)

When soap is added to a greasy substance, the hydrophobic tails are embedded in the non-polar fats and oils. However, the polar heads are attracted to the polar water molecules. Clusters of soap particles called *micelles* form with the nonpolar oil droplet in the center surrounded by many polar heads that extend into the water. Eventually all of the greasy substance forms micelles, which can be washed away with water. In hard water, the carboxylate ends of soap react with Ca^{2+}, Fe^{3+}, or Mg^{2+} ions and form an insoluble substance, which we see as a gray line in the bathtub or sink. Tests will be done with the soap you prepare to measure its pH, its ability to form suds in soft and hard water, and its reaction with oils.

From *Laboratory Manual for General, Organic, & Biological Chemistry,* Karen C. Timberlake. Copyright © 2002 Pearson Education, Inc., publishing as Benjamin Cummings. All rights reserved.

Detergents or "syndets" are called synthetic cleaning agents because they are not derived from naturally occurring fats or oils. They are popular because they do not form insoluble salts with ions, which means they work in hard water as well as in soft water. A typical detergent is sodium lauryl sulfate.

$$CH_3(CH_2)_{10}CH_2 - O - \overset{\overset{O}{\|}}{\underset{\underset{O}{\|}}{S}} - O^- Na^+$$

Lauryl sulfate salt,
a nonbiodegradable detergent

As detergents replaced soaps for cleaning, it was found that they were not degraded in sewage treatment plants. Large amounts of foam appeared in streams and lakes that became polluted with detergents. Biodegradable detergents such as an alkylbenzenesulfonate detergent eventually replaced the nonbiodegradable detergents.

$$CH_3(CH_2)_9 - \underset{\underset{CH_3}{|}}{CH} - \bigcirc - \overset{\overset{O}{\|}}{\underset{\underset{O}{\|}}{S}} - O^- Na^+$$

Laurylbenzenesulfonate salt,
a biodegradable detergent

In addition to the sulfonate salts, a box of detergent contains phosphate compounds along with brighteners and perfumes. However, phosphates accelerate the growth of algae in lakes and cause a decrease in the dissolved oxygen in the water. As a result, the lake decays. Some replacements for phosphates have been made.

Lab Information

Time: 2 hr
Comments: You will be working with hot oil and NaOH. Be sure you wear your goggles.
               Tear out the report sheets and place them beside the matching procedures.
Related Topics: Esters, saponification, soaps, hydrophobic, hydrophilic

Experimental Procedures

Wear your protective goggles!

A. Saponification: Preparation of Soap

> **Materials:** 150-mL beaker, hot plate, graduated cylinder, stirring rod or stirring hot plate with stirring bar, large watch glass, 400-mL beaker, Büchner filter system, filter paper, plastic gloves, fat (lard, solid shortening, coconut oil, olive or other vegetable oil), ethanol, 20% NaOH, saturated NaCl solution

Weigh a 150-mL beaker. Add about 5 g of fat or oil. Reweigh.

Add 15 mL ethanol (solvent) and 15 mL of 20% NaOH. *Use care when pouring NaOH.* Place the beaker on a hot plate and heat to a gentle boil and stir continuously. A magnetic stirring bar may be used with a magnetic stirrer. Heat for 30 minutes or until saponification is complete and the solution becomes clear with no separation of layers. Be careful of splattering; the mixture contains a strong base. Wear disposable gloves, if available. Do not let the mixture overheat or char. Add 5-mL portions of an ethanol–water (1:1) mixture to maintain volume. If foaming is excessive, *reduce* the heat.

Caution: Oil and ethanol will be hot, and may splatter or catch fire. Keep a watch glass nearby to smother any flames. NaOH is caustic and can cause permanent eye damage. Wear goggles at all times.

Obtain 50 mL of a saturated NaCl solution in a 400-mL beaker. (A saturated NaCl solution is prepared by mixing 30 g of NaCl with 100 mL of water.) Pour the soap solution into this salt solution and stir. This process, known as "salting out," causes the soap to separate out and float on the surface.

Collecting the soap Collect the solid soap using a Büchner funnel and filter paper. See Figure 1. Wash the soap with two 10-mL portions of cold water. Pull air through the product to dry it further. Place the soap curds on a watch glass or in a small beaker and dry the soap until the next lab session. Use disposable, plastic gloves to handle the soap. **Handle with care: The soap may still contain NaOH, which can irritate the skin.** Save the soap you prepared for the next part of this experiment. Describe the soap.

Figure 1 Apparatus for suction filtration with Büchner funnel

B. Properties of Soaps and Detergents

Materials: Test tubes, stoppers to fit, droppers, small beakers, 50- or 100-mL graduated cylinder, stirring rod, laboratory-prepared soap (from part A), commercial soap product, detergent, pH paper, oil, 1% $CaCl_2$, 1% $MgCl_2$, and 1% $FeCl_3$

Prepare solutions of the soap you made in part A, a commercial soap, and a detergent by dissolving 1 g of each in 50 mL of distilled water. If the soap is a liquid, use 20 drops.

B.1 **pH test** Place 10 mL of each soap solution in separate test tubes. Use 10 mL of water as a comparison. Label. Dip a stirring rod into each solution, then touch the stirring rod to pH paper. Determine the pH. *Save the tubes for part B.2.*

B.2 **Foam test** Stopper each of the tubes from B.1 and shake for 10 seconds. The soap should form a layer of suds or foam. Record your observations. *Save the tubes for part B.3.*

B.3 **Reaction with oil** Add 5 drops of oil to each test tube from B.2. Stopper and shake each one for 10 seconds. Record your observations. Compare the sudsy layer in each test tube to the sudsy layers in part B.2.

B.4 **Hard water test** Place 5 mL of the soap solutions in three separate test tubes. Add 20 drops of 1% $CaCl_2$ to the first sample, 20 drops of 1% $MgCl_2$ to the second tube, and 20 drops of 1% $FeCl_3$ to the third tube. Stopper each test tube and shake 10 seconds. Compare the foamy layer in each of the test tubes to the sudsy layer obtained in part B.2. Record your observations.

Report Sheet

Date _____   Name _____

Section _____   Team _____

Instructor _____

Pre-Lab Study Questions

1. What happens when a fatty acid is reacted with NaOH?

2. Why is ethanol added to the reaction mixture of fat and base in the making of soap?

3. Why is the product of saponification a salt?

A.   Saponification: Preparation of Soap

Describe the appearance of your soap.

Questions and Problems

Q.1   How would soaps made from vegetable oils differ from soaps made from animal fat?

Q.2   How does soap remove an oil spot?

B.   Properties of Soaps and Detergents

Tests	Water	Lab Soap	Commercial Soap	Detergent
B.1 pH				
B.2 Foam				
B.3 Oil				
B.4 CaCl$_2$				
MgCl$_2$				
FeCl$_3$				

Report Sheet

Questions and Problems

Q.3 Which of the solutions were basic? Why?

Q.4 Write an equation for the saponification of trimyristin with KOH.

Amino Acids

Goals

- Use R groups to determine if an amino acid will be acidic, basic, or neutral; hydrophobic or hydrophilic.
- Use paper chromatography to separate and identify amino acids.
- Calculate R_f values for amino acids.

Discussion

A. Amino Acids

In our body, amino acids are used to build tissues, enzymes, skin, and hair. About half of the naturally occurring amino acids, the *essential amino acids,* must be obtained from the proteins in the diet because the body cannot synthesize them. Amino acids are similar in structure because each has an amino group ($-NH_2$) and a carboxylic acid group ($-COOH$). Individual amino acids have different organic groups *(R groups)* attached to the alpha carbon atom. Variations in the R groups determine whether an amino acid is hydrophilic or hydrophobic, and acidic, basic, or neutral.

Some R groups contain carbon and hydrogen atoms only, which makes the amino acids nonpolar and hydrophobic ("water-fearing"). Other R groups contain OH or SH atoms and provide a polar area that makes the amino acids soluble in water; they are hydrophilic ("water-loving"). Other hydrophilic amino acids contain R groups that are carboxylic acids (acidic) or amino groups (basic). The R groups of some amino acids used in this experiment are given in Table 1.

Table 1 *Amino Acids Found in Nature*

R Group	Amino Acid	Symbol	Polarity	Reaction to Water
H—	Glycine	Gly	Nonpolar	Hydrophobic
CH_3—	Alanine	Ala	Nonpolar	Hydrophobic
⬡—CH_2—	Phenylalanine	Phe	Nonpolar	Hydrophobic
HO—CH_2—	Serine	Ser	Polar	Hydrophilic
$HOC(=O)$—CH_2—	Aspartic acid	Asp	Polar, acidic	Hydrophilic
$HOC(=O)$—CH_2—CH_2—	Glutamic acid	Glu	Polar, acidic	Hydrophilic
$H_2NCH_2CH_2CH_2CH_2$—	Lysine	Lys	Polar, basic	Hydrophilic

Ionization of Amino Acids

An amino acid can ionize when the carboxyl group donates a proton, and when the lone pair of electrons on the amino group attracts a proton. Then the carboxyl group has a negative charge, and the amino group has a positive charge. The ionized form of an amino acid, called a *zwitterion* or *dipolar ion,* has a net charge of zero.

$$CH_3(CH_2)_{10}CH_2 - O - \overset{\overset{O}{\|}}{\underset{\underset{O}{\|}}{S}} - O^- Na^+$$

In acidic solutions (low pH), the zwitterion *accepts* a proton (H$^+$) to form an ion with a positive charge. When placed in a basic solution (high pH), the zwitterion *donates* a proton (H$^+$) to form an ion with a negative charge. This is illustrated using alanine.

$$NH_2 - \overset{\overset{CH_3}{|}}{CH} - \overset{\overset{O}{\|}}{C} - O^- \quad \xleftarrow{\text{Base}} \quad \overset{+}{NH_3} - \overset{\overset{CH_3}{|}}{CH} - \overset{\overset{O}{\|}}{C} - O^- \quad \xrightarrow{\text{Acid}} \quad \overset{+}{NH_3} - \overset{\overset{CH_3}{|}}{CH} - \overset{\overset{O}{\|}}{C} - OH$$

Donates H+	accepts H+	
High pH (charge = 1–)	Zwitterion (neutral pH) (charge = 0)	Low pH (charge = 1+)

B.   Chromatography of Amino Acids

Chromatography is used to separate and identify the amino acids in a mixture. Small amounts of amino acids and unknowns are placed along one edge of Whatman #1 paper. The paper is then placed in a container with solvent. With the paper acting like a wick, the solvent flows up the chromatogram, carrying amino acids with it. Amino acids that are more soluble in the solvent will move higher on the paper. Those amino acids that are more attracted to the paper will remain closer to the origin line. After removing and drying the paper, the amino acids can be detected (visualized) by spraying the dried chromatogram with ninhydrin.

The distance each amino acid travels up the paper from the origin (starting line) is measured and the R_f values calculated. The R_f value is the distance traveled by an amino acid compared to the distance traveled by the solvent. See Figure 1.

$$R_f = \frac{\text{distance traveled by an amino acid (cm)}}{\text{distance traveled by the solvent (cm)}}$$

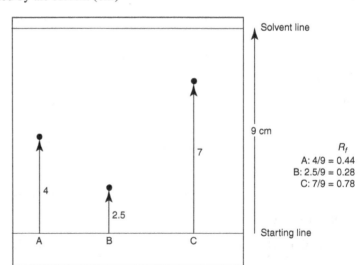

Figure 1   A developed chromatogram (R_f values calculated for A, B, and C)

To identify an unknown amino acid, its R_f value and color with ninhydrin is compared to the R_f values and colors of known amino acids in that solvent system. In this way, the amino acids present in an unknown mixture of amino acids can be separated and identified.

Lab Information

Time: 2 ½ –3 hr
Comments: Ninhydrin spray causes stains. Use it carefully.
                Tear out the report sheets and place them next to the matching procedures.
Related Topics: Amino acids, zwitterions

Experimental Procedures

 **GOGGLES REQUIRED!**

A. Amino Acids

Materials: Organic model kits or prepared models

A.1 Using an organic model kit, construct models of glycine and alanine. Draw their structures. Convert the alanine model to a model of serine. Indicate whether each of the amino acids would be hydrophobic or hydrophilic.

A.2 Form ionized (zwitterion) glycine by removing a H atom from the –COOH group and placing it on the N atom in the –NH$_2$ group. Draw the structure of the glycine zwitterion.

A.3 Write the structure of glycine in a base and in an acid.

B. Chromatography of Amino Acids

Materials: 600-mL beaker, plastic wrap, plastic gloves, Whatman chromatography paper
#1 (12 cm × 24 cm), toothpicks or capillary tubing, drying oven (80°C) or hair
dryer, metric ruler, stapler, amino acids (1% solutions): phenylalanine, alanine, glu
tamic acid, serine, lysine, aspartic acid, and unknown
Chromatography solvent: isopropyl alcohol, 0.5 M NH$_4$OH; 0.2% ninhydrin spray

Preparation of paper chromatogram Using forceps or plastic gloves (or a sandwich bag), pick up a piece of Whatman #1 chromatography paper that has been cut to a size of 12 cm × 24 cm. *Keep your fingers off the paper because amino acids can be transferred from the skin.* When this paper is rolled into a cylinder, it should fit into the chromatography tank (large beaker) without touching the sides. Draw a pencil (lead) line about 2 cm from the long edge of the paper. This will be the starting or origin line. Mark off seven points about 3 cm apart along the line. (See Figure 2.) Place your name or initials in the upper corner with the pencil.

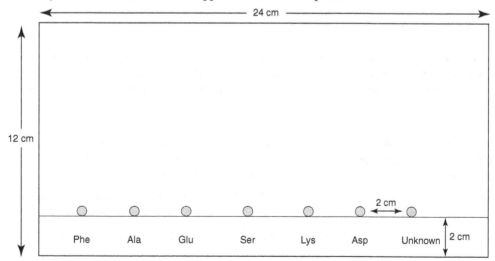

Figure 2 Preparation of a chromatogram

Application of amino acids Apply small amounts of the following 1% amino acid solutions: phenylalanine, alanine, glutamic acid, serine, lysine, and aspartic acid. Also prepare a spot of an unknown. Use the toothpick applicators or capillary tubes provided in each amino acid solution to make a small spot (the size of the letter **o**) by lightly touching the tip to the paper. After the spot dries, retouch the spot one or two more times to apply more amino acid, but keep the diameter of the spot as small as possible. A hair dryer can be used to dry the spots. *Always return the applicator to the same amino acid solution.* Using a pencil, label each spot as you go along. Allow the spots to dry.

Preparation of chromatography tank *Work in the hood.* Prepare the solvent by mixing 10 mL of 0.5 M NH₄OH and 20 mL of isopropyl alcohol. Pour the solvent into a 600-mL beaker to a depth of about 1 cm but not over 1.5 cm. (The height of the solvent must not exceed the height of the origin line on your chromatography paper.) Cover the beaker tightly with plastic wrap. This is your chromatography tank. Label the beaker with your name and leave it in the hood.

Running the chromatogram Roll the paper into a cylinder and staple the edges *without overlapping. The edges should not touch.* Slowly lower the cylinder into the solvent of the chromatography tank with the row of amino acids at the bottom. Make sure that the paper does not touch the sides of the beaker. See Figure 3. Cover the beaker with the plastic wrap and leave it undisturbed. The tank must not be disturbed while solvent flows up the paper. Let the solvent rise until it is 2–3 cm from the top edge of the paper. It may take 45–60 minutes. *Do not let the solvent run over the top of the paper.*

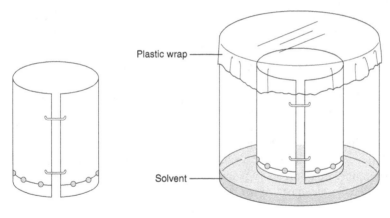

Plastic wrap

Solvent

Figure 3 Chromatogram in a solvent tank

Visualization of amino acids *Working in the hood*, carefully remove the paper from the tank. Take out the staples and spread the chromatogram out on a paper towel. *Immediately* mark the solvent line with a pencil. Allow the chromatogram to dry completely. A hair dryer or an oven of about 80°C may be used to speed up the drying process. Pour the solvent into a waste solvent container.

Working in the hood, spray the paper lightly, but evenly, with a ninhydrin solution. Dry the sprayed paper by placing it in a drying oven at about 80°C for 3–5 minutes or use a hair dryer. Distinct, colored spots will appear where the ninhydrin reacted with the amino acids.

Caution: Use the ninhydrin spray inside the hood. Do not breathe the fumes or get spray on your skin.

B.1 Draw the chromatogram on the report sheet, or staple the original to the report sheet. Record the color of each spot on the drawing or original.

B.2   Measure the distance (cm) from the starting line to the top of the solvent line to obtain the distance traveled by the solvent.

B.3   Outline each spot with a pencil. Place a dot at the center of each spot. Measure the distance in centimeters (cm) from the origin to the center dot of each spot.

B.4   Calculate and record the R_f values for the known amino acid samples and the unknown amino acid.

$$R_f = \frac{\text{distance traveled by an amino acid}}{\text{distance traveled by the solvent}}$$

B.5   **Identification of unknown amino acids** Compare the color and R_f values produced by the unknown amino acids. Identical amino acids will give similar R_f values and form the same color with ninhydrin. Identify the amino acid(s) in the unknown.

Report Sheet

Date _____   Name _____

Section _____   Team _____

Instructor _____

Pre-Lab Study Questions

1. What are the functional groups in all amino acids?

2. How does an R group determine if an amino acid is acidic, basic, or nonpolar?

A. Amino Acids

A.1	Structures of Amino Acids	
Glycine	**Alanine**	**Serine**
Hydrophobic or hydrophilic?		

A.2 Zwitterion structure of glycine	A.3 Glycine ion in base	Glycine ion in acid

Report Sheet

Questions and Problems

Q.1 Write the structure of the zwitterion of alanine.

Q.2 Write the prevalent form of alanine in an acidic solution.

B. Chromatography of Amino Acids

B.1 Chromatogram drawing or original, with colors of spots written in

Calculation of R_f Values

B.2 Distance from origin to solvent line: _____

Amino acid	Color	B.3 Distance (cm) amino acid traveled	B.4 R_f value
Phenylalanine			
Alanine			
Glutamic acid			
Serine			
Lysine			
Aspartic acid			
Unknown			

B.5 Identification of unknown # _____ : _____

/